Praise for KRONOS RISING: KRAKEN (vol. 3)

"A great finale to a brilliant series. Gripping from the word go and breathtaking all the way to the jaw-dropping climax. Max Hawthorne does it again, as only he can!"
–Peter Tonkin, bestselling author of 45 novels, including *Killer*

"Max Hawthorne's climactic finish to his award-winning Kraken trilogy latches onto you with all the power and ferocity of its legendary namesake and doesn't let go. A truly heart-pounding and well-crafted conclusion."
–G. Michael Hopf, bestselling author of *The End*

"The Kronos Rising: Kraken series requires a finale as big and bad as its name — and Hawthorne delivers. Fast and edgy, Kraken 3 pits strong protagonists against their most nefarious nemeses, with plenty of nail-biting action to keep you flipping pages."
–Kurt Anderson, author of *Devour* and *Resurrection Pass*

Praise for KRONOS RISING: KRAKEN (vol. 2)

". . . it takes some of the lessons nobody ever learned in Jurassic Park and ups the voltage exponentially . . .the ultimate aquatic smackdown, and it's gonzo good action fun."
–The Horror Fiction Review

"Kronos Rising: Kraken (vol. 2): 2018 Gold Medal winner" (action/ adventure category)
–AUTHORSdb

GH00538322

"*Master of Marine Terror, Max Hawthorne pens the perfectly crafted blockbuster, taking his readers on the thrill ride of their lives! To say that 'Kronos Rising: Kraken (Volume 2) is a 'page turner' is an understatement! Equally rivaling the likes of Crichton's 'Jurassic World', Benchley's 'Jaws' and Alten's 'MEG' book and movie franchises, 'Kraken V2' truly earns its proverbial place on the shelf! Hawthorne's 'Kraken V2' reads like a bullet train thrill ride from the first gripping page and takes you hostage until the explosive end! Hawthorne's original characters possess the dimension and sparkle, deserving of a cast of Hollywood's top A-list stars to bring them to life on the big screen! It's brilliant storytelling and THE way a story should be told! Now, that's entertainment!!!"*
–Kevin Sasaki, Media Representative

"*. . . unrelenting suspense, incredible action sequences, vividly realized characters, and unexpected plot twists that nail you to the page. Get this book immediately if you love a great sea monster story!*"
–Monster X Radio

Praise for KRONOS RISING: PLAGUE

KRONOS RISING: PLAGUE: 2016 Gold Medal Winner (horror category)
–AUTHORSdb

"*The entire horror universe now has a new writer . . . a delightful edge-of-your-seater, guaranteed to leave readers wanting to keep the lights on.*"
–YeahStub.com

"*Max spins another harrowing, action-packed monster tale, painstakingly researched, and rich in scenic and historic detail, while delivering the same true-to-form, page-turning intensity as always."*

–The Crypto Crew

Praise for KRONOS RISING: DIABLO

"Kronos Rising: Diablo, one of 2016's Top Ten Books!"

–AUTHORSdb

". . . the story retains Max Hawthorne's uncanny ability to make his monsters feel like characters in their own right, as well as his innate aptitude when it comes to invoking a sense of awe and wonder in the reader."

–Geek Ireland

"A riveting offshoot of the wonderful Max Hawthorne books, *Kronos Rising* and *Kraken*! Keeps the excitement and momentum of those stories going strong! More, more, more!!"

–Kevin Sasaki, Media Representative

Praise for KRONOS RISING: KRAKEN (vol. 1)

"It's *Jurassic World* on steroids . . . a fun, fast read even if you have to take the kids to the ball game and mow the lawn."

–From My Shelf Books

"*KRONOS RISING: KRAKEN* (vol. 1): 2016's People's Choice Award Winner & Book of the Year!"

–Geek Ireland

"Hawthorne's writing evokes a sense of awe and terror, tapping into a deeply-rooted and primal fear of the unknown. The Kraken possesses an otherworldly aura which is hard to describe, but it really makes your skin crawl."

– Sean Markey, DinoGuy

"While most authors would have played it safe and stuck to a formula emulating the successful elements of the first novel (think the "Meg" series), Hawthorne's vision is cast on a larger canvas. KRAKEN jumps ahead 30 years into the future, depicting a worldwide ecological shift in earth's oceans as a consequence of the events in the first novel. Hawthorne certainly knows how to tell and pace a fine adventure tale, in the tradition of Robert E. Howard."

– Cryptomundo

Praise for KRONOS RISING

". . . a master class in the suspension of disbelief. Kronos Rising is reminiscent of the work of Michael Crichton (Jurassic Park, Congo) in that it weaves together an exciting and gripping yarn which, despite depicting fantastical subject matter, doesn't insult the reader's intelligence by appealing to the lowest common denominator."

–Krank.ie

"*KRONOS RISING* by Max Hathorne; 2014's PIX Book of the Year!"

–Prehistoric Times Magazine

"Batten down the hatches and brace yourself . . . Hawthorne delivers suspense at a breakneck pace in his terrifying debut."

– Ryan Lockwood, Author of *Below*

"A word to the wise: if you bite your nails, you'd better wear oven mitts when reading *Kronos Rising*. It will drag you down to the depths of fear and take you back for a breath of air as fast as you can turn the pages. Readers beware: a new Master of Marine terror is in your bookstore, and his name is Max Hawthorne!"
–Stan Pottinger, NY Times Bestselling author of *THE BOSS*

"Kronos Rising takes readers on a roller coaster ride of gigantic scale. We're talking prehistoric big."
–Toledo Free Press

". . . a great addition to this genre, worthy of sitting on the shelf next to Peter Benchley's *Jaws*."
–Publisher's Weekly/Book Life

". . . a fabulous debut by Max Hawthorne. Simply put, it's got teeth. Big ones!"
–Chris Parker, screenwriter (*Vampire in Brooklyn, Battle of the Year, Heaven is for Real*)

"What a ride! An adrenaline pumping, non-stop descent into terror, *Kronos Rising* will do for this generation what "JAWS" did for the last one. Forget going *into* the water; I'm not going *near* it!"
–Mara Corday, sci-fi classic star of *Tarantula, The Black Scorpion*, and *The Giant Claw*

Praise for MEMOIRS OF A GYM RAT

"Max Hawthorne's raunchy, revealing memoir is certain to induce bouts of calorie-burning laughter, embarrassed grins, and reconsiderations of one's gym membership. A smutty and enjoyable exposé of life behind health club doors, *Memoirs of a Gym Rat* is both a scandalizing and edifying read."
–Foreword Clarion Reviews

MONSTERS
&
MARINE
MYSTERIES

MAX HAWTHORNE

For my dad.

"*For truth is a naked lady, and if by accident she is drawn up from the bottom of the sea, it behooves a gentleman either to give her a pink petticoat, or to turn his face to a wall and vow that he did not see.*"

-Rudyard Kipling, *A Matter of Fact*

ACKNOWLEDGMENTS

It is with tremendous pride and humility that I acknowledge the following individuals and/or organizations for their support and/or contributions to this book.

First, I'd like to give a big shout-out to a few of the radio/podcast hosts and personalities whose shows I've been privileged to appear on. That includes: Richard Syrett at *Coast-to-Coast AM*, Yaya Diamond from *Dream Chasers Radio*, Shannon "The Voice" LeGro at *Into the Fray Radio*, Mark Eddy at *Night-Light*, Craig Ansell, Chris Harmon, and Austin Burke over at the *3 Beards Podcast*, Solaris Blueraven from *Hyperspace*, Kat Hobson at *Fate Mag Radio*, Matthew Bennett at *Introspection*, Michael Hall from *Spaced Out Sundays*, Lauren Smith at *Nite Callers*, and Alex Greenwood from *Mysterious Goings On*. I'm especially appreciative of Kelly Steffen from the *Sky Door Network*, for offering me the chance to host my show on her network. It's a privilege and I'm looking forward to *Max Hawthorne's Monsters and Marine Mysteries* finally surfacing.

I'd also like to mention Kevin and Jennifer Malek, over at *Paraversal Universe*. A wonderful couple; I was featured on their show, back in 2019. Tragically, Kevin passed away unexpectedly this past year. He is sorely missed.

My undying gratitude to my indefatigable publishers over at *Far From The Tree Press*, both for stepping up and for always having my best interests at heart. It's good to be appreciated, and I look forward to future collaborations. I'd also like to give a special mention to Lana B., a talented artist who helped perfect the cover for *Monsters & Marine Mysteries.*

I'd be remiss if I didn't thank paleontologist Dr. Mark McMenamin and Berlin Ichthyosaur State Park for the use of their *Shonisaurus* fossil images. Also, my gratitude to Curt Jenner from the *Centre for Whale Research* for the use of his pygmy blue whale photos, Andrew Fox for the data he provided on wounded great white shark "Matilda", and Dave and Patricia Carlin for the use of frames from their Sanibel Island sea serpent video.

I would also like to express my appreciation to Jess Tudor for his shark bite research and use of related images, marine biologist Simon J. Pierce and intern Sofia Green for the use of their Galapagos whale shark images, and the *Discovery Channel* for the info published on their "Super Predator" documentaries. Also, thanks to Jason Zucker, Andrew Cocks, Jeroen van Valkenburg from *Monster Fish Taxidermy,* Yuri Grisendi from *Catfish World,* the *National Archives,* and the *British Columbia Scientific Cryptozoology Club* for the use of their assorted images, as well as the Facebook group *Carcharodon carcharias* for the use of their Orca video.

A huge shout-out to the following individuals who took the time to do interviews with me for this book, and who provided invaluable details in regard to their respective sightings: Rodney Ross (South Side Sea Monster), Paul George (Carnival Cruise Monster), Earl Stoessiger (Garry Liimatta's turtle), Dave Carlin (Sanibel Sea Serpent), Demetrius (Octopus giganteus), and Jack Pendell (Whale of a Shark).

My sincere appreciation to assistant editor Adam Michael from *The Gettysburg Times* for taking the time to get me the archived images I needed, Lana B. for her digital editing skills, former NY Jet Anthony Corvino for his white shark mount image, Jeff Shaw from *Bone Clones* for the bite measurements from their white shark jaws, Steve Roesch for his cryptid research and suggestions, and Brett Manning for her drawing of the "fairy" my daughter and I encountered.

A special mention to the late Garry Liimatta, one of the few people in recorded history to acquire film footage of an actual "sea monster" (his 38-foot turtle). Also, my eternal gratitude to Garry's widow, Elizabeth Waring, for allowing me to use still images from his Super-8 footage for my analysis.

As always, I'd also like to express my gratitude to my Grammar Nazi-slaying editor, Willis Beyer, for taking the time to review this book. Thank you for giving my manuscript that last bit of spit-and-polish that every novel needs.

Of course, a nod to our two enormous Siberian forest cats, Mace and Olaf. Thank you for hogging my desk – I mean *keeping me company* – when I write. And for the occasional ambush while I'm headed to or from the kitchen.

Last, but certainly not least, to my incredibly supportive family, especially my anime-loving daughter Ava, my everlasting devotion. And to my readers, including the always enthusiastic (but not always patient) *"LEGIONS OF KRONOS,"* thank you for putting up with me and my monsters.

There's plenty more to come.

-Max Hawthorne
"Prince of Paleofiction"

In days of old,
When knights were bold,
And steel ships did not exist.
Things often got frantic,
When crossing the Atlantic,
And the Kraken, it got pissed.

-Max Hawthorne

IF SEA MONSTERS EXIST, WHERE ARE THE BODIES?

When it comes to cryptids, it's one of those inevitable questions. It's often posed by those who doubt the existence of unknown animals or deride the efforts of cryptozoologists who strive to prove they exist: "Where are the bodies?"

More often than not, that question is tailgated by: "If Nessie exists, there has to be a breeding population, right? I mean, it's not immortal. So, why haven't we found a carcass?"

In point of fact, these are fair and logical questions, so let's address them. It is 100% true that if a species is to continue, there must be a viable breeding population. Otherwise, it would vanish in the evolutionary blink of an eye. And, as they are indeed *not* immortal, we should expect to find bodies.

Or should we?

I suppose it depends on the cryptid in question. Since the majority of this book focuses on unproven marine species, let's focus on those. The ocean is a vast place. As we've seen over the last few years, several new species of large (body size 7-8 meters) marine organisms (i.e. Beaked whales and Orcas) have been discovered.

How is that possible? These are big, air breathing mammals, not some secluded species of tiny Amazonian tree frog. They've undoubtedly been around a long time – probably longer than our species has. Yet, we've only come across them in the last decade. How can that be? Where have they been hiding all this time?

Admittedly, the aforementioned species of sub-Antarctic killer whale was observed in a hostile environment not often traversed by tourists – off Cape Horn. Observations and tissue samples from the 2019 pod proved that there were significant differences between them and all known Orca species. Their heads and dorsal fins were different and their white "eye" markings much smaller. But from a distance, and to an untrained observer, it is likely they would be mistaken for one of the other known sub-species of Orcas.

Of course, *any* large, air breathing marine animal could be mistaken for a whale when viewed from a distance. Perhaps even something that isn't mammalian.

Let's consider the possibility that there is a relict population of one or more species of mosasaur still roaming our oceans. True, it's incredibly unlikely. And if they *are* out there, how are they concealing themselves? We have boats, satellites and drones. Why isn't footage of them appearing on the evening news?

To begin with, as I mentioned, the oceans are almost incomprehensibly huge. How huge? To put things in perspective, let's do some math. A mile is 5,280 feet. And a cubic mile is a cube measuring 5,280 feet per side (think four Empire State buildings perched atop one another). The world's oceans contain 321,003,271 cubic miles of water. That's right, 321 *million* cubic miles (and change). And, when it comes to exploring all that space, only 5% of the sea *floor* has been mapped out. That doesn't include the average 12,100 feet of water extending vertically above said bottom.

That's some serious real estate.

If seen from the deck of a boat, it is likely that a mosasaur would be misidentified as a whale. You'd see a large, dark form surfacing for air which would quickly submerge. It might just be a silhouette even. You wouldn't know it was any different than, say, a finback whale. Unless, of course, you were right on top of it.

Additionally, if mosasaurs (effectively, huge marine monitor lizards) surfaced for air like sea turtles or crocodilians, they most likely would not spout, per se. There would be no explosive release of water vapor to draw one's eyes or ears like when a whale blows. Sea turtles and crocs release the breath they're holding in silent streams of bubbles, making their surfacing far less noticeable than that of your average blue or sperm whale.

It is also possible – even probable – that mosasaurs, like extant sea snakes, were (or is it are?) able to absorb a percentage of their oxygen through their skin. If so, they would need to surface far less often to breathe. Consider modern sea turtles. By slowing their heart rate, marine chelonians are capable of traveling underwater for several hours. And while resting, they can take naps on the bottom for up to seven hours.[*]

That's a long time.

---

[*] https://ocean.si.edu/ocean-life/reptiles/sea-turtles

Next comes the matter of stealth. As predators, mosasaurs would probably fall into the same category white sharks do when it comes to interacting with other predators, including their own kind. Their hierarchy may well be based on size. It's a documented fact that smaller great whites make way for larger ones. Therefore, it is logical that a *Tylosaurus*, for example, would give ground before a bigger, more fearsome predator.

Forced to live in seas whose surfaces are littered with noisy, metal monsters, i.e. ocean liners, naval vessels, and cargo ships (not to mention nuclear submarines when beneath the surface), it is likely predatory marine reptiles would be instinctively skittish when detecting disturbances like the deafening turbulence caused by a ship's props. Their response would most likely be to submerge and/or flee the area. There have been many mosasaur sightings over the last few decades. And many of these have been from boats that were either drifting, anchored up, or using sails as a means of propulsion.[*]

This tends to support the notion that "sea monsters" tend to avoid potentially dangerous, power-driven vessels.

If we consider the story of the mosasaur-like creature harpooned, killed, and melted down by the whaling vessel *Monongahela*[**], the whalers were able to approach the animal and harpoon it using rowed whaleboats. There were no engines to propel them. Additionally, based on the behavior said sea serpent reportedly exhibited, I believe it was extremely ill, perhaps even dying. Otherwise, it is likely their attempts to get close enough to bury their irons in its flesh would have failed miserably.

Then, there's the question of witnesses. All of the New Zealand sightings listed on the link above took place from shore or from the deck of a vessel (rarely, from Jet Skis). But there are none that I'm aware of in which a surfer, snorkeler, or scuba

[*] http://nzcryptozoologist0.tripod.com/id22.html

[**] http://anomalyinfo.com/Stories/1852-march-captain-seaburys-serpent

diver came face to face with something resembling a sixty-foot crocodile with fins instead of legs. Then again, with a grown man being the same size as a juicy porpoise, perhaps such encounters have happened and the witnesses simply didn't survive to tell the tale.

Lastly, let's formally address the "where are the bodies?" issue. It is a known fact that extant crocodiles ingest stomach stones (known as gastroliths) to help offset their innate buoyancy. A lungful of air makes it hard to submerge. Big game hunters know all about this; if they shoot a crocodile in the water, they must retrieve it at once or the carcass will sink and be lost. Hence, most croc hunts take place while the reptile is sunning itself on the river bank.

We also know via the fossil record that marine reptiles such as plesiosaurs and pliosaurs ingested gastroliths – sometimes hundreds of them. It is quite possible that mosasaurs did too. If so, and if there are any of them still roaming our oceans, their bodies would sink upon death. Their remains would not drift with the tide and end up washing ashore. They would fall all the way to the sea bottom, where the inevitable would take place via scavenging sharks, hagfish, crustaceans, etc. The carcass would be stripped of flesh and, soon, all that remained would be a skeleton. After fifty or a hundred years, even that would be gone.

That said, there is considerable evidence that suggests there are undiscovered or, rather, *unproven* species of large marine animals still roaming our oceans. Garry Liimatta's giant turtle is, in my opinion, an almost certainty. The question remains: how do we capture one, or at least lure it into camera range?

Without ending up on the menu, of course.

THE CARNIVAL CRUISE MONSTER – PART 1

As an author specializing in paleo-fiction-based "marine terror" novels, my bread and butter comes from writing about primeval sea monsters. Novels are works of fiction, of course, but as a passionate angler, the sea will always hold a special place in my heart. That said, when an opportunity arises to read up on or, even better, investigate a sighting of what may have been an *actual*, undocumented marine beast, I'm all in.

A few years back, I was approached on social media by a young man who experienced a sighting he wanted to share with me. He'd told friends about it in the past and regretted it, but he was hopeful that, with my background, I would take him seriously. His name is Paul George and he hails from the UK. During the summer of 2014, Paul was working on as a fitness trainer on a Carnival Cruise Lines cruise ship known as the *Carnival Breeze*. He was stationed was on the upper deck of his vessel when he and several guests spotted an enormous marine organism swimming alongside.

The *Carnival Breeze*, docked in Cape Canaveral
(photo by Max Hawthorne)

I spoke with Paul at length about the incident via Facebook Messenger. We discussing his sighting and, later, he sent me a few emails as well. Although his story is of an anecdotal nature (he has no photos or video to corroborate the incident), I found Paul sincere and his story believable. I have some experience with storytellers, having interviewed over fifty thousand people in my previous career, so I have a knack for picking up inconsistencies.

That said, I'm giving Paul the benefit of the doubt. Most encounters with unknown animals, or "cryptids", as they're known, are fleeting and happen unexpectedly (I know, it's happened to me), and the witness is often so startled that they freeze up and forget to attempt to document the experience.

In Paul's case, he actually had a photo of the animal as it veered off, but his cell phone was lost at the next port-o-call.

Initial Conversation (online)

I'm going to allow Paul to describe what I've dubbed "The Carnival Cruise Monster" in his own words, via our initial online conversation:

Paul: *"...when it surfaced it was like a submarine where the water runs off of it. But this animal was almost flat and not round like a submarine. I'd say it looked rectangular or oval. But it was thick! It was clearly very powerful. But it seemed to just be relaxing as it went by us."*

Max: "The way you described the water running off it implies an animal of large size. When you say 50 feet did you have anything to compare it with to get that estimate? And was that the body or the overall animal?"

Paul: *"I honestly think I am being conservative by saying that. I've seen our life boats in the water next to us and they are pretty large, but this was larger. Even from our distance everybody agreed it was whale sized. But it wasn't long and thin like a whale. That was just what we saw. I don't think we saw all of it."*

Max: "Interesting. Did you see any other parts? Was there a tail? Did it have limbs, legs, fins or flippers? And how big are the lifeboats?"

Paul: *"I only saw the main body and briefly the head, or at least what I think was the head. It didn't show all of itself by any means. The lifeboats are large enough to fit 150 people on but I don't know the length in feet. It was just very slowly swimming by. As if it was just seeing what we were. It didn't even seem bothered. So, no means of propelling itself. We watched it for maybe 30 seconds. It was definitely swimming, but not exerting itself. The water was* *moving around it tho. Whatever it used to swim stayed under water."*

Max: "Interesting. If it was a turtle the paddles would've been visible."

Paul: *"It can't have been a turtle but that's just what it reminded me of."*

Max: "Let's talk about the head. Can you describe it?"

Paul: *"A huge body. The head came up just once and only briefly. But it looked thick and long. This was a big animal and I'm sure I didn't see all of it."*

Max: "Did you see the head or just a neck?"

Paul: *"I think it was the head. It must have been 10 feet long from the bit I saw. The neck seemed the same length and thick too I'm sorry if this isn't helping but it was a while ago."*

Max: "Did you see any features? Meaning eyes, nostrils, teeth, anything? BTW, a 150-person lifeboat is 9.6 meters, or 32+ feet

Paul: *"Honestly no. Just the outline of the head. It was starting to get dark. The lifeboats are large yeah, this was much larger tho. That's the only size comparison I can think of."*

Max: "Did it have scales, or was the skin smooth? And what color?"

Paul: *"It was smooth mainly, but possibly some lines on it. Dark grey or black. And shiny."*

Max: "Sorry to be a pain. I appreciate you trying the best you can."

Paul: *"You're not a pain. It's nice to tell someone. Most people tell me it was a whale. But it wasn't."*

Max: "You said it was definitely not a turtle of some kind. What makes you think so?"

Paul: *"I've never known of a 50 ft turtle! Plus, it didn't have a shell."*

Max: "I ask because leatherbacks have lines on their back. But the size is impossible. How do you know there was no shell?" (at this point, I sent Paul a photo of a juvenile Leatherback sea turtle that was black, with distinctive lines and stripes)

Max: Like this?

Paul: *"The black shiny bit looks right! But wrong shape and no white. Plus, the head was massively bigger."*

Max: "How would the shape be different?"

Paul: *"Less rounded. Less tapered in at the rear. But I'm not even sure I saw the whole body. Just what broke the surface."*

Max: And was the head larger in proportion to the body? Was it a different shape?"

Paul: "Much larger! It was longer and thicker."

Max: "Interesting. So, you think maybe just the front of the animal broke the surface."

Paul: *"Whatever this was it was a powerful animal. It didn't look like it was all at the surface. Maybe the head and upper back we saw."*

Max: "Important question: did it breathe at all? Meaning did you hear an exhale or see it blow like a whale or was it quiet?"

Paul: *"Well I'd say so as it was at the surface for a while and its head came out for a moment like it took a breath. The water around its head went white for a moment but I didn't hear a blow-hole sound or anything."*

Max: "Hmm."

Paul: *"It wasn't a fish. No way. And I'm certain it wasn't a whale."*

Max: "What shape was the head? Like a turtle, like a crocodile? Like something else? Was it oval or tapered or triangular?

Paul: *"This may seem mad but we all said it looked like a crocodile head only bigger. Not as slender. Just very thick."*

Max: "Is there any chance it was some sort of squid? And maybe the head was a piece of tentacle?"

Paul: *"No way! I know what squids look like and I've never known them to be black or this shape. Whatever this was it was heavy, I mean really heavy looking."*

Max: "I believe you. One more question, would you say it was a mammal or a reptile?"

Paul: *"No idea! It had a thick black hide tho. Like a manatee or something, but not loose. Very tight. A bit like that turtle in that picture. If that turtle was all black with a larger head and a more square shape and was whale sized then I'd say it was a turtle."*

At this point, I asked Paul to send me an emailed statement, summarizing his sighting.
(via email)

Paul: *"A few years ago, I worked as sports and fitness staff on cruise ships. On my last contract, I was working on the top deck one day on the Carnival Breeze. It was around August or September in 2014. Our home port was Miami and we were sailing from there towards Mexico, if I recall. It was early evening around 7-8 pm and I was introducing the movie on the big screen.*

Towards the port side of the ship I noticed a few people were beginning to talk quite excitedly and gather around each other. They were pointing at something in the water. I was only a few yards away, so I went to see what the fuss was. When I got amongst the crowd I looked over and saw what I can only say was an unknown sea creature. It was swimming quite calmly right by the ships side and was directly beneath where we were looking from deck 12. I think it was curious and checking us out. I briefly thought it was a whale but very quickly realised it wasn't. It was black and shiny with what looked like tight, thick, leathery skin. It was quite square at the shoulders which looked like the main portion we could see. It was big! If I had to guess from what was above the water, I'd say it was 50 ft long at least. I'm using the ships life boats as a comparison here, I often saw them by the ships side and they are 30ft long approximately. Plus, I'm only going off the portion of the animal I saw, the tail (if it had one) never broke the surface. It could have been much longer. Because it was a broad animal (it was over half as wide as it was long) I honestly think there was more to the length we never saw. Plus, the head was massive. We only saw the head for a moment, it looked like it raised it up to take a gulp of air and then it submerged again. But the head was long too, maybe 10ft itself and over half as wide also. I never saw the teeth, as it was below us we only saw it from above. The neck was thick and powerful too. As crazy as it seems I'd say it looked fairly similar to a massive turtle but with a much bigger head. It was clearly a very powerful creature and I can't get over how thick it looked. It was very robust. I never saw if it had arms or flippers unfortunately but it was propelling itself as it was swimming against the current slowly away from us. We only got to see the head and the upper back but it was a very impressive animal. We watched it for about 30 seconds. Because there were small waves it made it difficult to see very clearly and it was tough to make out too much detail. All I can say is that I spent the best part of 4 years working on cruise ships and saw many whales, sharks and other known sea animals. This was like nothing I'd seen before. The group of passengers looked to me to see if I knew what it was, there was a group of about 10 people and myself. I had to say that I had no idea and none of them did either. We just watched this animal swim by us as if it was relaxing in the twilight. As we were in the middle of the sea and nobody could get phone reception, I don't think anybody had their phones to record it. I did though and I took a couple of pictures as it was trailing off. But I lost that phone in one of the ports soon after. To this day I still don't know what we saw that evening. But we all walked away in agreement that we had witnessed something special."

Follow-up questions

I found my initial conversation with Paul, as well as his emailed summary, to be very interesting. I gave him a few follow-up questions.

- Can you describe the shape of the head in more detail, meaning was there any extant animal that it was reminiscent of, and if not, the general shape? (oval, triangular, rectangular...)
- Is there any way for you to check your employment records and try to get a more accurate idea of the date?

- Any idea how far out at sea you were, or how many days it had been since you'd left port?
- Do you know anyone on the ship that might have photos?

Paul: *"Yeah sure. It was black and smooth like the body and I would say a cross between a turtle and crocodile?! Sounds weird but it was smooth, but long like an alligator or something, just not bumpy. All I know is the dates of my contract (July 14-December 14). But this was nearer the start than the end. I'm sure it was end of summer time. It was still hot. And this was a sea day I remember that, so we would have been quite far from land*. I was the only one I know of who got photos. None of the guests I was with had their phone. I'm sorry if this is a bit vague but I'm trying."*

After these initial talks, I spoke with Paul several more times via Messenger, and got more details from him. I mentioned the "Super Predator", and suggested that, if his sighting did represent an unknown or undocumented creature, it might well be the same species. His response was: *"This might sound silly, but a 9 ft shark wouldn't fill this thing up!"*

Note: As part of my investigation, I checked the speed of cruise lines and found out that, while underway, standard vessels travel at an average of 20 knots (23 mph). High-speed ships are faster.** Based on how Paul described the animal effortlessly keeping pace with the *Carnival Breeze*, it would definitely be capable of chasing down and catching a fleeing three-meter great white like "Shark Alpha".

Although I wasn't doubting him, in the interest of being thorough, I sent Paul additional videos and photos of an assortment

---

* (Note: in a later conversation I confirmed with Paul that the ship's position at this time was far out at sea, in the middle of the Gulf of Mexico)

** https://www.cruisecritic.com/articles.cfm?ID=2978

of whales taken by drone (dorsal views), to see if any of the body shapes were a match. This included sperms, humpbacks, and even beaked whales. He laughed and said, as big as they were, "whales weren't robust enough to be this thing."

After looking over everything at that point, I decided to email Paul a quick sketch I did of possible head and body shapes, based on his descriptions.

Via email

Max: Hey (Paul), please check out the attached sketch. Trying to give you some options to look at, and to see if any of them is close to what you saw. I gave you variants in terms of head, shape, size, body size, etc. Please see if any of the come close, and feel free to print and tweak one if you think it is close but needs some work. Letter "F" had some bubbling behind it to give you choices for that but it got cut off when I snapped the pic. Just do the best you can, please, and thank you.

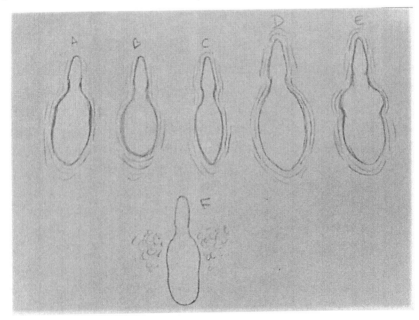

Sketch by the author.

Paul: *"So, the water was foaming a bit to the side of the animal, but not right next to it but a few feet away. The waves weren't big so I guess that could be from its method of propulsion? It was always on our port side. It kept pace for as long as it wanted to it seemed, like it wanted a closer look at us. But it wasn't looking like it was struggling to keep pace and I think it could have gone faster. But after 30 seconds or so it just kind of veered away and fell behind until we couldn't see it anymore. And the picture 'E' looks pretty similar actually! The big strong shoulders definitely look right. And the head looks good too. But I'd say it was slightly bigger as in wider. I hope I'm being descriptive enough."*

Follow-up Interview

After receiving his emailed response, I resumed interviewing Paul via Messenger and focused on the size of the creature in his sighting. He asked me a question I've gotten quite a few times over the years:

Paul: *"So, you truly think a remnant pliosaur population still exists??"*

Max: "I believe there are may be large marine reptiles out there that are 'extinct', but nobody told them. Your animal, and I'm taking everything you told me on faith, of course, could be a pliosaur or a mosasaur."

Paul: *"Hahahaha! Ok."*

Max: "Or something we've never documented."

Paul: *"I don't know what it was. I have thought many times about what it might have been. But I'm not educated enough to have a guess. However, like I said, it was as big as a whale but not a* whale. And I don't know (what) else there is that's whale sized! But picture E is very close! The shoulders especially."

Max: "But if the head and upper back measured 50 (feet) your creature would be very large."

Paul: "I can't speculate on how long the entire thing was, but what I think is that because we only saw it until maybe halfway down it's back, that's why it looked square in shape. Make sense?"

Max: "Absolutely. When a croc surfaces much of it is draped under the water and hangs down."

Paul: "Holy crap!!! You just nailed it! That's exactly what it looked like! A crocodile chilling in the water. But black and smooth instead. I just got goosebumps."

Max: "Yeah. You would not want to be in the water with that thing."

Paul: "No way! But they can't get that big. Maybe a deformed whale?! I dunno. You know about this more than me."

At this point, Paul sent me his sketch of what he saw.

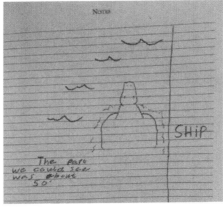

Paul George's sketch of what he saw swimming
alongside the *Carnival Breeze*.

Max: "Wow, that would make the head more like 15′ without the neck. Oh, did you see eyes or anything?"

Paul: *"The neck was a bit longer I think, it's not perfect. But I hope it is ok. I'm rubbish at drawing! I didn't see eyes no, I just put those dots there where I thought they should be. The head only came out the water for a moment. Also, the small waves next to where the arms I guess would be are meant to show a bit of water disturbance. However, the shoulders were broad and it's body was thick. I've seen whales and this body was much thicker than them."*

Max: "Interesting. Amazing, actually. What kind of whales?

Paul: *"I couldn't tell you. I saw them when we sailed around New Zealand about 5 years ago. But I'm certain this wasn't a whale. Everybody with me was sure it wasn't a whale. It was a much more solid animal."*

Max: "It sounds like it. I'm going to tweak your sketch and send it to u and see what u think in about an hour. Let me know if it's closer."

Paul: *"Ok mate."*

Max: "Btw, did this creature's body break the surface completely? Was the head above water fully, a portion of it and the neck, or just under the surface? That would change how you viewed it."

Paul: *"Only the upper back was above the surface, only a couple of feet above. The head came up a few feet for a moment then went back to being just below. Most of the animal was just below the surface."*

Max: "Would you say the head was fully visible? Could it have been curved down at the neck so that a portion of it was underwater? Like arched a bit?"

Paul: *"The head I think was fully visible only for a moment. I'd say it's body was curved downward too, but at the rear."*

Additional drawings

I found Paul's sketch interesting because he made it a point to show the disturbance on the water around the animal. This made sense to me in terms of whether it was using flippers of some kind to propel itself along and keep pace with the ship. I sent him two images based on his own sketch.

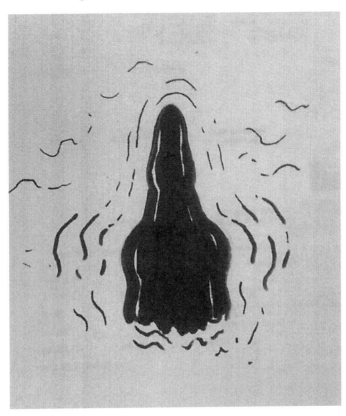

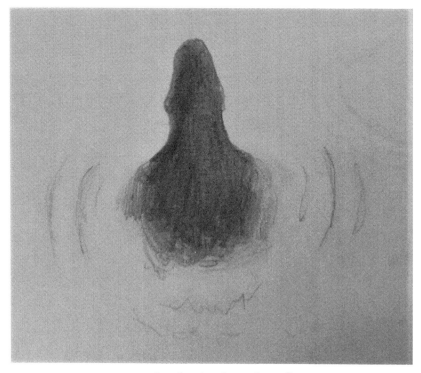

Sketches by the author

Paul: *"Both very good! But the body was a bit wider. Maybe I did see flippers and I'm getting confused thinking it was shoulders. The second one is really very good to be fair!"*

Max: Keep in mind, if the exposed part represents 50′ we're talking about an enormous animal. The overall skull/mandibular length could be 15 feet without the neck. I'm not trying to exaggerate; I'm basing it on your drawing."

Paul: *"Is that big then?? How big would that make the whole thing?"*

Max: "A pliosaur with those proportions would have an overall length of around 25 meters or 80 feet. A mosasaur would be longer due to the crocodile-like tail."

Paul: *"Blimey!!! Is that possible?"*

Max: "Like I said, there have been historical sightings (by whalers) of mosasaur-like creatures measuring over 100 feet. No physical proof, but eyewitness reports. One was 115-120, so I don't see why not."

Paul: *"Why aren't these things seen more often?? Low numbers, intelligence?"*

Max: "A combination, I suspect. There are very few grizzlies compared to bison in this country, and whales are effectively bison. The animal would often be mistaken for a whale. You were above it not on a small boat. Probably instinctively cunning. You approach a croc on a boat what does it do? Submerge and vanish."

After the Interview

After our interview, Paul and I had an extended conversation on everything from monster squid to the Megalodon shark (I was pleased to discover that he had read my article on adult Megalodons being obligate scavengers and found it quite plausible). I also spoke to a few artists about the sighting, including Andrew Cocks, a renowned paleo-artist and sculptor whose work hangs in museums, and Walt Disney animator Jason Zucker. Andrew produced several sketches based on the sighting, and Jason was so intrigued by the story that, after reading it twice, he produced a rendering of how he felt the animal looked.

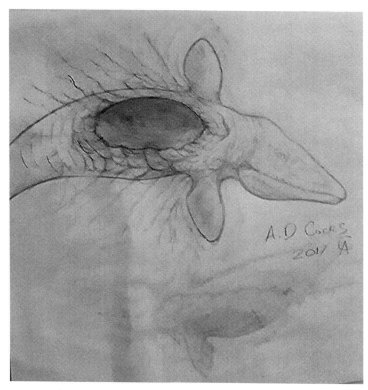

The "Carnival Cruise Monster" by Andrew Cocks

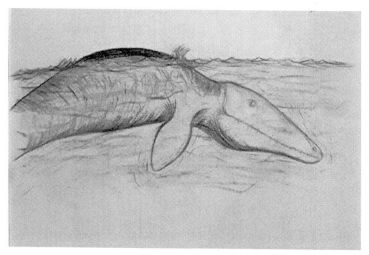

Artist's sketch of a possible side view of the "Carnival Cruise Monster" based on witness description. Artwork by Andrew Cocks.

"The Monster", an artist's depiction of the Carnival Cruise Monster, by
Walt Disney animator Jason Zucker.

After taking everything into consideration, the only potential "hole" I found in Paul's story was the lack of proof. Although people traveling on holiday often have their cell phones glued to their hips and even take pictures of their food, I've been on cruise ships. On the uppermost deck where this happened, and where you'd most likely be lying in the sun in a bathing suit and popping in and out of the pool and Jacuzzi, phones are rarely on one's person. (at least, less so in 2014, as they weren't waterproof yet) And phones do get lost. That's unfortunate, because with a picture to back it up, Paul's story would have been international news.

However, I still find him sincere. His story makes for an interesting account and jibes with numerous eyewitness reports of sea monsters that have been described as a "giant turtle without a shell".

I would also point out that, if this sighting is accurate, it makes me rethink my notions of how marine reptiles surfaced for air. In my novels, I have pliosaurs blowing like whales – huge funnels of compressed water vapor, exploding from their blowholes. It makes for a dramatic visual, but what if that's wrong? If you watch a video of a crocodile or sea turtle surfacing, you will see how quiet they are when coming up for air.

Might this behavior explain the white water/bubbles around the creature that Paul observed? It would seem so. And, if so, would it not make it even tougher for someone to spot one of these things if, when it does come up to breathe, it makes no noise whatsoever?

Also, what he interpreted as "shoulders" were most likely the animal's pectoral fins, extended like the diving planes on a submarine, to stabilize it as it swam. Without fore-flippers undulating up and down as a means of propulsion – as they would have been if the creature in question was some sort of plesiosaur or turtle – I can only assume that it was propelled by its caudal fin.

This suggests a mosasaur-like animal. Such a body design would also explain the animal's submerged rear portion and tail being concealed from view (if mosasaurs surface for air in a crocodilian manner, and there is no reason to assume they didn't). With the snout and forequarters angled upward, and the hindquarters and tail draping down, water clarity would account for what the witness discerned.

Granted, Paul's account is fantastical (and admittedly similar to a scene in *Kronos Rising: Plague*, where a prowling pliosaur paces a cruise liner before snatching a passenger off its railing). Still, it makes for an intriguing tale, with fascinating possibilities.

THE CARNIVAL CRUISE MONSTER PART 2:

Did a Living Mosasaur Stalk the Ship?

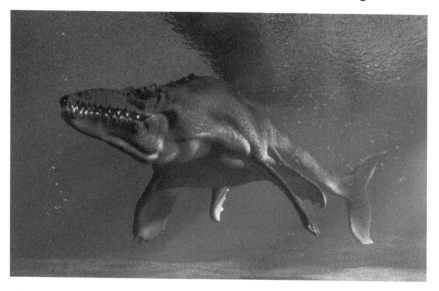

My 2017 interview with Paul George, the affable UK resident who spotted an enormous, unknown marine creature from the upper deck of the *Carnival Breeze* in 2014, was intriguing. The notion that a giant and, as yet unidentified, "sea monster" could exist in our oceans, let alone show itself in broad daylight while keeping pace with a cruise liner in the middle of the Gulf of Mexico, is enough to stir anyone's imagination.

A few months after our initial interview, and after conferring with a few cryptozoologists who had questions of their own, I decided to do a follow up with Paul. We'd left things a little ambiguous, and my hope was to revisit his sighting and see if there was anything we missed, and also to review other possible explanations for what he observed. Although we were working with something that is technically an anecdotal sighting, I attempted to come to a sort of "formal conclusion" as to what the Carnival Cruise Monster might have been.

Or perhaps *is*.

If you've read any of my novels, you know that pliosaurs are my passion. But as much as I'd like to believe that there is a relict population of them eking out an existence somewhere, the odds are astronomically against it. According to the fossil record, the genus has been gone for ~ninety million years. Moreover, Paul did not describe any perceivable flipper movements near the front of the animal he saw. That is an important detail. I should think any fore-flippers paddling would have been obvious. That tends to eliminate a member of the *Plesiosauridae* as a candidate.

After sending Paul dorsal views of every large whale species I could find, including a rare beaked whale, I have concluded that what he observed was not a cetacean. This is based not only on his outright rejection of the assorted whale images, but the fact that he observed that when the animal surfaced for air the water around its head turned white right before it broke the surface. There was no spouting, as a whale does. Rather, its exhalation started below the surface, like those of sea turtles and crocodilians typically do. For crocodiles, this is done for purposes of concealment, and for a stealthy marine predator it makes sense.

With the Carnival Cruise Monster apparently propelled by some sort of tail or caudal fin, it appears that the only remaining candidates are a mosasaur or marine crocodile of some kind.

The color and texture of what Paul saw tends to rule out the latter – prehistoric marine crocs like *Dakosaurus* are believed to have had scaly skin – so a mosasaur seems most likely. They were still alive during the Chicxulub impact, 65 million years ago – nearly 25 million years after pliosaurs are believed to have gone extinct. They were also huge, with fragmentary fossil evidence of such species as *Hainosaurus, Mosasaurus,* and *Tylosaurus* suggesting they may have reached nearly sixty feet in length. Additionally, I have a huge mosasaur jaw in my collection that bears the bite mark of an even larger specimen – one that exceeded seventy feet in length. This makes a seagoing monitor lizard like a mosasaur a strong contender.

To better explore this possibility, I sent Paul a piece of paleo-art depicting a mosasaur leaping out of the water (sideview). This is a transcript of our conversation:

Max: "Hi (Paul). Might a dorsal view of something like this be what you saw? The paddles might explain the shoulders, but don't let me brainwash you. If it was turtle-like that's fine."

Paul: *"Hey mate. This in all honesty still seems too streamlined. The head looks about right, but I'm sure this things body was more robust."*

Max: "Seen from above it could be broader, I would imagine. My question really boils down to, was it broad like a turtle, or were the front fins spread out at angles so that, when seen from above, it created the appearance of a dark, wider body. Again, not trying to brainwash u."

Paul: *"If what I saw were fins then they were thicker and stronger. This thing I saw seriously looked like it had traps!"*

Max: "One sec, let me do a quick sketch."

29

I grabbed a pencil and paper and did my best to create a likeness of the shadowy form he had described to me via his sketch and during our previous interviews.

Paul: *"Exactly like that!!!! That's it!"*

Max: "Interesting. one minute"

Paul: *"Imagine that, completely jet black. A foot above the small waves, water running off it. That's what it was"*

Max: "One more sec."

I then added a dotted line around the form I'd sketched, in an effort to show what its shape might have been without poor water clarity and failing light obscuring it.

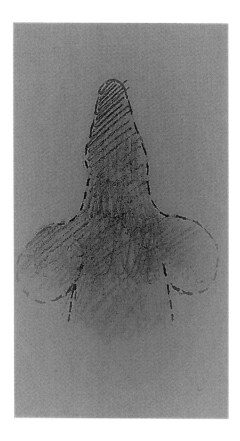

Max: "If I take into account the angle pectoral fins might have had, this is what it would be without the water obstructing. It really does look like some sort of heavy-bodied mosasaur of some kind."

Paul: *"I see. That could have been how it was positioned then."*

Max: "Don't let me brainwash you. I don't want to hear some asshat saying I did. All that matters is (that) the first sketch (sans outline) matches what you saw.

Paul: *"It was cruising. It wasn't making any effort to keep pace. So, it may have had its fins relaxed by its side. Don't worry, I know the shape of what I saw. The first picture really does look like it."*

Max: "Good. If you take the actual painting I sent first today, picture just the top of the body showing and the fins spread out to the side, like a shark's. They're mainly for steering. The propulsion comes from the tail, which is like a shark's, but inverted. With the animal being black, seen from above, those flared fins would stick out like shoulders. Like padded shoulders on a suit. It was going in a straight line so the fins would (probably) be angled to maintain position near the surface.

Paul: *"That could've been it. I never saw the back end of it. I think that was angled down. I only saw to about half way down it's back, I think. Makes sense. But I still say that if it is an ancestor of this animal, it's gotten bigger built over the years."*

Max: "It was probably doing this"

(I then sent him this image of a submerged crocodile)

A crocodile floating just beneath the surface (image: public domain).

Max: "With the head angled down a bit to keep an eye out for rivals. Or dinner."

Paul: *"I think that's exactly what it was doing. Which is crazy cos it was as fast as our ship without making any effort."*

Max: "They were the top predators at the end of the Mesozoic. It would make sense, between raptorial whales and assorted mega-toothed sharks coming and going – creatures it would have competed with – that it grew substantially. Large, blubber rich, warm-blooded prey would provide a lot of nutrients. And mosasaurs were growing steadily at the end of the Cretaceous. All the big sharks were extinct by then, but mosasaurs were still getting bigger."

Paul: *"Trust me, this thing could eat anything it wanted for breakfast! The thing I remember the most is just how robust and powerful it looked. Like it wasn't bothered about anything. I think that's the main thing we all said. It was just chilling out."*

I thanked Paul at this point for his time and for having the courage to reach out to me.

Paul: *"One day it will all come out, I guess. Someone will find something. Either a new bone or an alive animal. Just hope they don't go extinct."*

Max: "Tell u what, if I can go after one on rod and reel, I'll invite you to come along. If ur game"

Paul: *"Haha! We would need 100 men to pull the thing I saw onboard. Maybe more!"*

A few days later, I came across a piece of paleo art from an unknown artist and sent Paul the image to gauge his response.

Max: "Maybe this is what you saw... Note the fins out to the sides that, submerged, could create the illusion of extra width or shoulders..."

Paul: *"What is that???"*

Max: "A *Mosasaurus hoffmani.*"

Paul: *"It could very well be it. It looks robust enough"*

Max: "If u picture it seen from above you've got a huge, croc-like head, a thick neck and massive body."

I spoke to Paul one last time, after he'd listened to my interview on Monster-X Radio, wherein I'd discussed his sighting at length. During the interview, cryptozoologist Scott Mardis asked me whether the lifeboats attached to the ships could have been used as a reference for size comparison. I told him I didn't know exactly where the lifeboats were on the ship, but I imagined with them being a substantial distance from the water, forced perspective would make them appear much larger and eliminate them from being a useful barometer of the animal's mass. Paul confirmed this:

Paul: *"Btw, the lifeboats are on deck 4 But u can't see them from 12 as they are below deck 5 which was the promenade deck and wrapped around the ship."*

Max: "Thank you, that is good info to know as I plan on doing a follow up piece on the sighting."

In summary, I found nothing from my follow-up conversations with Paul George that detracted from the genuineness of his story. He seems sincere and reliable and I believe he saw what he says. *What* he saw, of course, remains to be seen. Personally,

I believe that, based on available evidence, and after having eliminated every known species I can think of, as fantastical as it sounds, an extant mosasaurid appears to be the most likely candidate.

It's not like there is no precedent for this kind of thing. There have been numerous sightings of creatures like this. The most dramatic is probably the Monongahela Incident, wherein a 19th century whaling crew harpooned, killed, and processed a "sea serpent" measuring over 100 feet in length. I believe, and Paul did also, after he read that piece, that the animal must have been either sick or dying to allow them to approach it like that.

The Monongahela incident, as incredible as it sounds, rings true for multiple reasons. The details the captain provided of the animal are astounding. They took all body measurements, analyzed the color and thickness of its blubber and how it burned once rendered into oil, and even counted its teeth. A pretty sophisticated hoax by even today's standards.

But there two points that stand out as being very strong indicators of the account's authenticity. The first is that, when said sea serpent was butchered, they discovered that it was an air breather and that one of its lungs was longer than the other. As Scott Mardis pointed out during our interview, this is a known characteristic of snakes*, which Mosasaurs are closely related to.

The second is, as I pointed out, the animal's tail was described as having ended in "flat, firm cartilage". The Monongahela incident took place in 1852. We didn't know that many mosasaurs had hypocercal tails with a bi-lobed caudal fin like that of a shark until the 21st century.***

---

* https://www.ncbi.nlm.nih.gov/pmc/articles/PMC4282204/

** https://www.nationalgeographic.com/news/2013/9/130910-mosasaur-sea-monster-reptile-tail-ocean-science/

In short, it is distinctly possible that some sort of giant, whale-eating marine reptile still roams our oceans. If so, it has outlived the dinosaurs and outlasted Megalodon. And if Paul George got to see one – luckily from a safe distance – he is an incredibly lucky man.

THE GARRY LIIMATTA SEA MONSTER: IS IT THE REAL DEAL?

One of the most incredible sightings of an unidentified sea creature took place in May of 1969, when angler Garry Liimatta and a friend of his were headed out of Kyuquot Channel, from Vancouver Island, BC. From fifty feet away, Garry watched a huge, unknown marine animal frolicking on the surface. He was an experienced boater and fisherman and immediately realized he was privy to something unknown.

Unlike in most sightings, Garry managed to get some footage of it using his trusty 8mm camera (then "state-of-the-art"). The film remained hidden until 1991 and, although dark and grainy, provides a tantalizing look into this unusual sighting.

First, let's look at the details of the encounter via an excerpt from a letter by the late Paul LeBlond, featured in the *British Columbia Scientific Cryptozoology Club's Newsletter*, dated July, 1992:

GIANT SHELL-LESS TURTLE SEEN OFF VANCOUVER ISLAND

by Paul LeBlond

On a fine morning of May 1969, fisherman Garry Liimatta was heading out of Kyuquot Channel (see accompanying map) towards offshore fishing grounds. Weather conditions were excellent: good visibility and a light sea. His boat was less than half a mile offshore when he saw on the port (left) side an animal which played around in circles for a few minutes, rolling, exposing side flippers and part of its head, after which it left northwards at a terrific speed. The animal came within 50 ft or less of the boat, and Liimata and crewmate Earl Stoesinger had a good look.

Map showing Vancouver Island and the area of Liimatta's sighting, at point marked x and indicated by an arrow.

©1992 British Columbia Scientific Cryptozoology Club's Newsletter
(used with permission)

Although Garry passed away in 2012, Earl Stoessiger, the man who was with him, is still with us. I was lucky enough to get in touch with Earl and did an in-depth interview with him. As someone with decades of experience on the water, I am quite thorough when it comes to asking the right questions. Earl's testimony cleared up a few discrepancies pertaining to the original sighting report, and also added some interesting details to it.

The first point of contention is that the original report gives the impression that both men were on the same boat (Earl is referred to as Garry's "crewmate"). Per Earl, they were not. They were in two separate boats. Garry's was the 36-foot *Anna*

L., and Earl's was the 38-foot *Sea Pride III*. Both boats were of similar design: wooden fishing boats with wheelhouses up front and cabins belowdecks.

It's interesting to note the size of the two mens' boats. The familiar length of their vessels gave Garry something to use as a reference to gauge the size of the animal they encountered. If you drive a 20-foot boat for years and a shark swims by that is easily the same length as your boat, you can accurately discern that it was at least 20 feet long. If it was a tail-length longer, even bigger.

The two men in their respective boats left out of Walter's Cove, located on the NW side of Vancouver Island, in Kyuquot Sound. It was first light when they headed out. They turned left (east) out of the cove heading for a fishing spot they referred to as "Grassy". There was no storm front, the weather was good and the sea was flat calm. This is important, as it made conditions optimal for the sighting that was to come.

The fishing grounds known as Grassy were a good 2-3 miles from the cove, situated along the fishing banks outside in Kyuquot channel. Their target was spring salmon and fishing was expected to be good. Grassy was between Vancouver Island and Tattoo Point and was known as a shallow spot where fish tended to congregate. The water in Kyuquot channel is typically around 30 fathoms deep (180 feet), but on Grassy it ranged from only 12-14 fathoms (72-84 feet).

Garry and the *Anna L.* were perhaps a quarter-mile ahead of Earl and his boat, and around a half-mile from shore, when things got exciting.

The two men carried portable CB radios. Per Earl, all of a sudden, Garry radioed him in a panic. He was going on and on that he was looking at a "sea monster" and asked Earl to come quickly.

I should interject a point about the Super-8 camera that Garry used to film the creature. Earl confirmed that not only did his friend have such a camera, but that he was very passionate about using it. He was constantly filming things and we are lucky that was the case.

Back to the sighting . . .

By the time Earl covered the 440 yards to Garry's location, the creature had submerged. Garry stopped filming and pointed excitedly at a section of water between the two men's boats. He asked Earl if he'd seen the creature while it was still on the surface, then pointed at something directly beneath them.

Mid-point between the two boats was a rock pile – a large upcropping of stone that rose up, forming a near-pinnacle from the nearby sea floor. Where the stones started to rise up the depth was around 10-12 fathoms (60-72 feet) and quickly shallowed up to as little as 6-8 fathoms (36-48 feet).

Laying on top of this reef – and covering a large portion of it – Earl saw a huge, shadowy form. It was stationary, and he described it as being a pale gray or grayish-white in color. It stood out starkly against the reef and was every bit as big as his 38-foot boat.

The two men milled around the area, waiting to see what would happen, with Garry watching the creature (I can only assume it was either eating a salmon or resting – sea turtles are known for doing things like that). Earl began circling the area, when Garry suddenly radioed him and told him it was gone.

This jibes with the initial account, including the part where a boat is seen about 200 feet away, along with Garry's description of the animal leaving at "terrific speed". Presumably, he was looking right at the creature when it left from the reef and departed the area. Per Earl's testimony, Garry stated it took off to the north.

I would also point out that Earl had encountered and was familiar with leatherback sea turtles, including their body shape, size, etc. He confirmed that the shadowy form beneath them was not a leatherback. It was a bit slimmer, appeared to have no shell, and was far too large. At first, he thought that it was a gigantic sea lion or something like that. When they got back to shore Garry took the time to make a quick sketch of the creature he'd seen. It had a build similar to a sea lion with the head of an enormous sea turtle. As he put it, "I think I saw an oversized turtle without a shell."

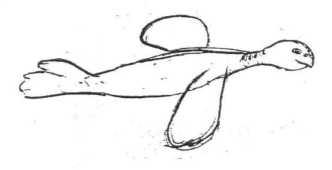

Sketch, by Garry Liimatta, of the animal he saw off the northwest coast of Vancouver Island

Sketch by Garry Liimatta. Image credit: British Columbia Scientific Cryptozoology Club's Newsletter, dated July, 1992. (used with permission)

Let's focus on Garry's film now, as it is hugely important.

When I initially viewed the footage, including a few stills from it, I got the distinct impression that the animal in the video was a reptile of some kind – possibly an extant pliosaur of sorts (sadly that turned out to not be the case, but hope springs eternal). But that was mainly because, due to deterioration of the original film, the stills showed it appearing more or less silhouetted; it didn't offer any revealing details.

The sketch Garry Liimatta made of the creature does give it a distinctive, turtle-like appearance. And it matches his description.

That said, given the fact that the animal was mostly submerged and/or rolling around, I couldn't help but wonder if Garry had truly seen what he described. Water refraction and glare can play tricks on the human eye. Assuming that the sighting wasn't an elaborate hoax (based on careful perusal of the footage, and after interviewing Earl Stoessiger, I am quite sure it wasn't), the inevitable doubts popped into my head.

Did Garry misidentify the animal? Could it have been an elephant seal, cetacean, or an enormous leatherback turtle? There are big ones out there. I have personally seen the drifting carcass of a loggerhead that dwarfed the current world record of 1,200 lbs.

I decided to do some investigating. I took it upon myself to enhance a few stills of the Liimatta creature, to see if anything "showed itself." To my surprise, it did, and in a way that was far more dramatic than expected.

I started off with the ambiguous still shown below. I began lightening and enhancing it, then started increasing clarity in an attempt to show hidden details. The moment I took that step, the image that jumped out at me told me that Garry's account was correct.

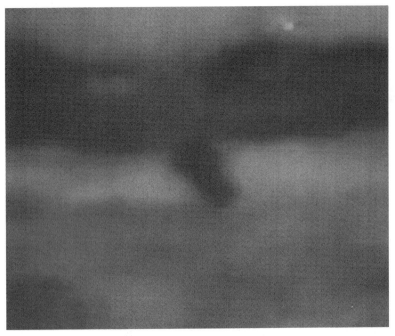

Still from Liimatta footage. Used with permission.

What he'd witnessed was some sort of enormous, shell-less turtle. Look closely. Can you see it? You're looking at the animal's head and neck, not a flipper as some have stated. You can see the distinctive shape of the eye, the brow ridges, the nostrils, a large beak (with a considerable overbite), and even the thick ridges of skin running down its neck.

I've inked lines onto the enhanced and enlarged image and put it side-by-side with an unlined copy to show it more clearly.

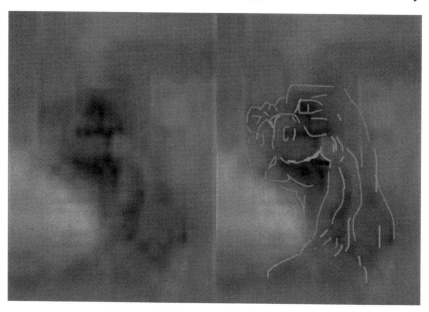

Closeup of Liimatta still enhanced (left),
with added outlines (right). Used with permission.

With this accomplished, I then went about the process of adjusting the contrast of the still-frame even more. I wanted to see the main structures. Much was lost, but you can now see that the deeply shaded areas that remain are indicative of the key features of a huge chelonian. You can see the recessed eye under a brow-like upper brow ridge and eyelid, thick ridges of skin from the lower eyelid directly underneath the orbit, the lower jaw (in shadow under the beak), and, again, those thick folds of skin running down the sides of the neck. The animal also appears to have been turning its head slightly toward the left, presumably looking in Garry's direction as it was being filmed.

That last part is a little bit frightening. The odds are the creature was actively feeding on large salmon and possibly even seals. I can't help but wonder if it was looking at Garry as a prospective meal.

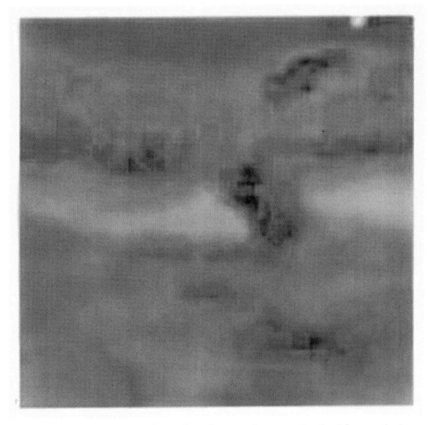

Further lightened frame from the Liimatta footage. Used with permission.

Oh, well. Let's go even lighter now...

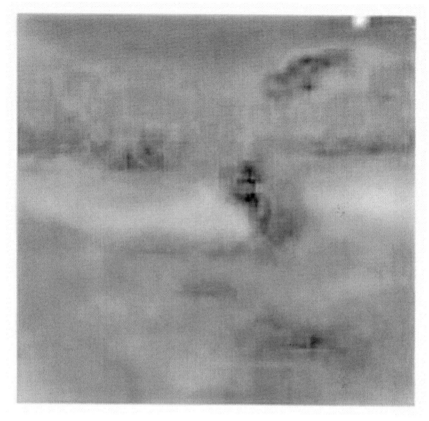

Even more lightened. Used with permission.

At this point, the image is incredibly grainy, but the structure remains. In fact, if you know what to look for, it literally jumps out at you (pun intended). Now, let's compare those stills to images of extant sea turtle. Notice the head of the green turtle below as it peeks above the surface. Granted, the neck isn't as long, but we're seeing similar behavior. Note also the large, dark eyes, the thick lower eyelid, and the large upper jaw and beak, overshadowing the lower jaw.

A sea turtle raises its head above the water to survey its surroundings.

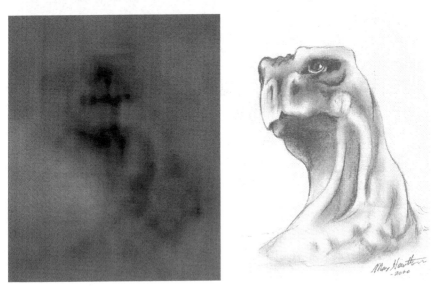

Still from the Liimatta footage with a sketch by the author,
attempting to show details.

Above, is an attempt on my part to do a pencil sketch based on the enhanced still. Understandably, some people have a hard time making out the details. Hopefully, this makes things stand out a bit more. I find it interesting that the turtle appears to have heavy brow ridges, almost like horns. This might explain other sightings where "sea serpents" were described as having small horns on the top of their heads.

Now, let's look at this sea turtle, mugging for the camera. The eyes, the brow-like upper eyelids, the undershot lower jaw almost hidden under the beak, the lower eyelid... All these characteristics exist in the enhanced still from the Liimatta footage. In fact, based on both Garry and Earl's statements, the skin color in this turtle is probably close.

As part of my research, I decided to watch the original video again, but this time with this new information in mind and using the HD setting on my computer. I encourage you to do the same. Under these conditions, the shape of the animal's face literally pops out at me. We can now see that what we are see-ing is definitely a living animal. Although moved by the current/waves, it is able to hold position using its flippers. And we can discern that it has a longer neck than a normal sea turtle and is able to do what cetologists (scientists that study whales) call "spy-hopping" – using its flippers to keep its head above water as it peers around.

Armed with this newfound knowledge, I decided to do a sketch of Garry's creature, based on his account, sketch, and footage, as well as my enhanced stills. He described the creature as being 38 feet long with an 8-foot neck (I assume that meant head and neck combined, as both are visible). He said it had large front flippers, no shell, and based on the "blotchy white and gray" description, it must have had skin similar to that of a leatherback, albeit a light-colored one. With divers added for scale, this is what I came up with:

Now, lest anyone roll their eyes or claim that such an animal is impossible, keep in mind that new marine animals are discovered all the time, including Orcas and Beaked whales, and sightings of giant turtles go back centuries.

I also took the liberty of adding in a cropped portion of the enhanced film image onto my drawing for ease of comparison. The insert plainly shows that the features from the film match those of the drawing; the eyes, beak, throat – everything fits.

My conclusion? Garry and Earl most likely stumbled upon a giant relative of today's leatherback sea turtle. Garry described it as fast-moving. Leatherbacks have been clocked at 22 mph[*] and they can dive to incredible depths (over 1,000 meters).

How heavy would such an animal be? Scaling up from a known weight of 1,500+ pounds for a 7.2' individual, a leatherback 38 feet in length would weigh in excess of 100 tons (they are massive). However, Garry described his creature as being only 6' across the body. He may not have seen its entire girth, of course, But its overall physique was more or less confirmed by Earl Stoessiger, who said he initially thought it was a colossal sea lion based on his overhead view of it. Of course, we know from the footage that it was not a sea lion, but slimming it down is necessary in order to get an accurate weight estimate.

If I go by a Steller's Sea lion which, at 10 feet in length weighs in at 2,000 lbs., we come up with a scaled-up mass of around 60 tons. That's still huge. However, a bull Steller's is massively built and I'm inclined to think that as a piscivore (fish eater) that was capable of "terrific speed" (as Garry described it) his turtle was slimmer than that. A leatherback 38' in length would have a shell 15' across, but again, he estimated his animal at 6' wide.

The most likely candidate available for comparison is probably the California sea lion *Zalophus californianus*. The less

---

[*] http://scienceblogs.com/deepseanews/2008/08/08/why-do-leatherback-turtles-div/.

robust and more streamlined females of the species are known to reach 6' in length and weigh 220 lbs. By using one of them as a mass model and scaling up, we reach what I believe is a more accurate weight estimate of around 28 tons.

Slimmer, yes. But we're still talking about a very large animal, folks. In terms of diet, it would probably eat fish, but it might also be an omnivore, feeding on marine plants, cephalopods (mainly squid, and possibly giant squid), and jellyfish. Some jellyfish get enormous; the Lion's Mane jellyfish, for example, can grow to over 120 feet in length. It would make sense for something to have evolved to prey upon it.

Last, but not least, there is one matter I haven't touched on – one that several readers have brought to my attention. That is the matter of reproduction. If what Garry saw was an overgrown turtle, why aren't we seeing them lumbering ashore to lay their eggs?

A fair question.

True, the prehistoric sea turtle *Archelon* most likely laid its eggs on shore, like extant sea turtles. But there's a big difference between a three-to-four-ton *Archelon* dragging itself up onto the beach and a near-thirty-ton monster doing so. Besides the physical constraints of not having seawater to support its tremendous bulk, one would think that such a sight would certainly be noticed by people.

But as the famous quote goes, "Nature finds a way". And that way takes the form of a different means of giving birth. It has long been accepted that plesiosaurs and ichthyosaurs gave birth at sea to live young, and mosasaurs are believed to have done so as well. But in June of 2020 a paper titled, *A giant soft-shelled egg from the Cretaceous of Antarctica*[*] gave evidence that a large creature (possibly a mosasaur but this was not confirmed) had laid the egg – an egg that was thin-shelled and

_____

* https://www.nature.com/articles/s41586-020-2377-7?fbclid=IwAR1TEX YP6lUoc9g0gSV33-vkJntGLV7QHfbj5JdUBCBTPRc4DCtx0bYGWuA

designed to hatch immediately upon being expelled into the water. This may have applied to mosasaurs and/or it may have also applied to a form of sea turtle, one that broke through the evolutionary and anatomical barriers that keep turtles oviparous (egg laying). Viviparous animals give birth to live young, and ovoviparous animals lay eggs that hatch inside the mother's body and are born alive. It is possible this huge turtle does the next best thing; laying eggs, but eggs designed to be torn open by the hatchlings at the moment of their birth. The fossilized egg would have obviously been stillborn, i.e. a dud.

Is there anything in the fossil record?

I find the footage Garry Liimatta shot to be quite compelling when it comes to proving this creature's existence. When it comes to supporting it further, however, one question that often arises is, "Is there anything in the fossil record to suggest such a creature's existence is possible?"

The answer is quite possibly.

The aforementioned turtle *Archelon* had a shell like the leatherback. There were also other giant soft-shelled turtles at that time, like *Ocepechelon* and *Protostega*. It is not beyond the realm of possibility that one of these giants survived the Cretaceous extinction event and evolved over the next 65+ million years. Said species' size may have increased over time to allow it to defend itself against predators like the *Otodus* line of mega-toothed sharks, and its anatomy may have changed to enable it to function as a speedy hunter.

An even more promising possibility might be *Pacifichelys urbinai*, a large sea turtle known from the Pisco Formation of Peru (Parham and Pyenson 2010)*. A mid-Miocene species, it is currently estimated to have lived from 15.97 to 11.6 mya.

---

* http://fossilworks.org/bridge.pl?a=taxonInfo&taxon_no=165652

Pacifichelys was durophagous, which means it used crushing jaws to consume hard-bodied prey. As a potential ancestor of *Titanichleys*, an active predator that hunts something other than jellyfish makes a lot more sense. Moreover, a comparison of the only known skull of the species to the enhanced still imagery does suggest a resemblance to the turtle Liimatta filmed back in 1969.

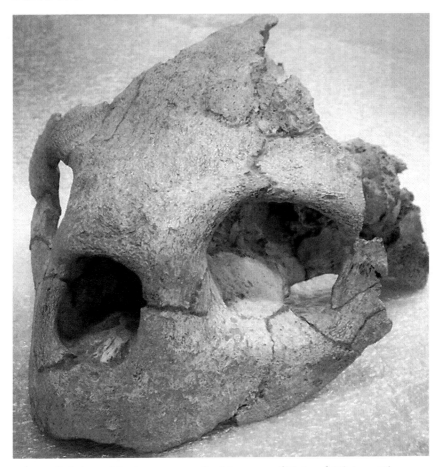

Pacifichelys urbinai. Image credit: Museum of Natural History, Lima.
Ghedoghedo (Creative commons)

In summary, based on the enhanced stills from the film footage (and after re-watching the HD footage) I am convinced that Garry Liimatta had the good fortune to observe and film an unknown chelonian – likely the biggest species of all time. If said creature is as he described it, it is most likely an aggressive and fast-moving animal, one able to defend itself from marine predators like sharks and Orcas (leatherbacks are known to attack and even chase sharks that attempt to prey on them). It would also most likely be, like its smaller (presumed) relative, the leatherback, an endothermic (warm-blooded) marine reptile. This would enable it to roam and hunt in cold water, including the extreme deep.

Now all we have to do is get footage and a tissue sample from one.

Hopefully, without getting eaten.

HAVE MEGA-TURTLES BEEN RESPONSIBLE FOR OTHER HISTORICAL MARINE CRYPTID SIGHTINGS?

There is no doubt in my mind that Garry Liimatta and Earl Stoessiger had an encounter with an enormous chelonian of some kind. In fact, I went so far as to assign it a scientific name. But have there been other sightings of such a creature? Could it be that some of the well-known anecdotal reports of "sea monsters" were, in fact, encounters with examples of this same species? And if so, is it dangerous to people?

Think about it. Many reported sea monster sightings describe creatures with a long neck, a "head like a horse" and/or a "mane". We know that *Titanichelys liimattii* behaves in some ways like other sea turtles. It engages in spy hopping, i.e. raising its head above the surface of the water to see what's going on above it. It was studying Garry Liimatta when he was filming it.

We also know that *Titanichelys* has a proportionately longer neck than that of other marine turtles, partly because of its lack of a rigid shell. This could explain the vertically-held necks/ heads that are sometimes described. It is highly unlikely that such sightings are extant plesiosaurs, i.e. *Elasmosaurus*, as we know that, anatomically, their necks were incapable of doing the "periscope thing". Also, when viewed head-on, a sea turtle does have a sort of equine look about it. Those big, doleful eyes and the visible nostrils.

Lastly, you can bet that cephalopods are stable fare for a huge and hungry sea turtle like that. And many sea turtles eat jellyfish. It's feasible that a big turtle, viewed at the surface as it scarfed down a frantically struggling squid, octopus, or Portuguese man-o-war, might give off the impression of having a "mane"; the mane being the prey item's writhing tentacles.

Let's review some historical sightings that may be a fit for Garry's turtle.

The HMY *Osborne* incident

On June 2, 1877, the royal yacht *Osborne* had an encounter with a massive marine creature, while sailing off Sicily's northern coast. Four members of the crew, including her captain, filed a report on the incident. That of Lieutenant William Haynes reads as follows:

"On the evening of that day, the sea being perfectly smooth, my attention was called by seeing a ridge of fins above the surface of the water, extending about thirty feet, and varying from five to six feet in height. On inspecting it by means of a telescope, at about one and a-half cables' distance (300 meters), I distinctly saw a head, two flappers, and about thirty feet of an animal's shoulder. The head, as nearly as I could judge, was about six feet thick, the neck narrower, about four to five feet, the shoulder about fifteen feet across, and the flappers each about fifteen feet in length. The movements of the flappers were those of a turtle, and the animal resembled a huge seal, the resemblance being strongest about the back of the head.

I could not see the length of the head, but from its crown or top to just below the shoulder (where it became immersed), I should reckon about fifty feet. The tail end I did not see, being under water, unless the ridge of fins to which my attention was first attracted, and which disappeared by the time I got a telescope, were really the continuation of the shoulder to the end of the object's body. The animal's head was not always above the water, but was thrown upwards, remaining above for a few seconds at a time, and then disappearing. There was an entirely absence of 'blowing' or 'spouting'. I herewith beg to enclose a sketch showing the view of the 'ridge of fins', and of the animal in the act of propelling itself by its two fins.'

The "Ridge of Fins" seen from HMY Osborne.
Plate from *Land and Water*, 1877

The creature seen from the HMY Osborne. Plate from *Land and Water*, 1877

When the *Osborne* returned to port her captain, Commander Hugh Pearson, filed an official report. Excerpts from it appeared in June 14th edition of *The Times*.

---

* Bernard Heuvelmans, *In the Wake of Sea Serpents*

"At about five o'clock in the afternoon of [June] the 2nd, the sea being exceptionally calm, while the yacht was proceeding round the north coast of Sicily towards Cape Vito, the officer on watch observed a long ridge of fins, each about six feet long, moving slowly along ... The fins were progressing in an eastwardly direction, and as the vessel more nearly approached them, they were replaced by the foremost part of a gigantic sea-monster. Its skin was, so far as could be seen, altogether devoid of scales, appearing rather to resemble in sleekness that of a seal. The head was bullet shaped, with an elongated termination, being somewhat similar in form to that of a seal ... Its features were only seen by one officer, who described them as like those of an alligator. The neck was comparatively narrow, but so much of the body as could be seen, developed in form like that of a gigantic turtle, and from each side extended two fins, about fifteen feet in length, by which the monster paddled itself along after the fashion of a turtle."*

On June 30th, a newspaper known as *The Graphic* printed a letter Lieutenant Haynes sent in as a follow-up to the *Osborne's* encounter.

"(The fins) were of irregular heights, and extending about 30 or 40 feet in line ... in a few seconds they disappeared giving place to the foremost part of the monster. By this time it had passed astern, swimming in the opposite direction to that we were steering, and as we were passing through the water at 10.5 knots, I could only get a view of it, 'end on', which I have shown in the sketch ... Its head was occasionally thrown back out of the water, remaining there for a few seconds at a time. It was very broad across the back or shoulders, about 15 or 20 feet, and the flappers appeared to have a semi-revolving motion, which seemed to paddle the monster along ... From the top of the head to the part of the back where it became immersed, I should consider 50 feet, and that seemed about a third of the whole length. All this part was smooth, resembling a seal. I cannot account

for the fins, unless they were on the back below, where it (was) *immersed.*"[*]

Based on the witness's description and sketches, the *Osborne* creature sounds very similar to Liimatta's turtle. The seal-like description of the body, paddles, and shape of the head are all apropos. It would have been a larger example, of course, if its head was, indeed, six feet long as the captain described. In fact, in some aspects, it also matches the description of the *Carnival Cruise Monster*, except it doesn't have an alligator-like head and uses paddles to swim.

I suspect this creature may well have been a *Titanichelys liimattii*. Perhaps the size was exaggerated a bit, at least parts of it. It's hard to accurately gauge the size of something from one thousand feet away when viewed through a spyglass, especially with only the waves as reference.

One thing I am fairly certain of, however, is the source of that "ridge of fins". The size and pattern scream one thing to me:

Orcas.

The line of fins was undoubtedly the collective dorsal fins of a pod of *Orcinus orca*. Put another way, I suspect the turtle was being attacked by an opportunistic pod of killer whales.

The descriptions bear out my theory. The fins submerged and then were replaced by the "foremost part of the monster". That suggests that the Orcas submerged as they launched their attack, and the turtle was struggling for the surface as the battle wore on. The description of the creature's head being "thrown back" for several seconds at a time, coupled with the sketch showing its head, flippers, and portions of its back coming up out of the water, are strong indicators that it was being mauled by sharp killer whale teeth.

Sea turtles don't swim with their fins out of the water, they swim submerged. Nor do they hold their heads and flippers out of the water, flailing around like that. But if one was seized by

---

[*] Bernard Heuvelmans, *In the Wake of Sea Serpents*

the rear of its body (hind limbs, tail, etc.) and was being bitten and torn at, that would have that effect. Killer whales are smart. They avoid the business end of any large creature they attack. They're also known for seizing the flukes of huge baleen whales – even the mighty blue whale – and pulling back on them as part of their strategy to exhaust their prey.

I believe that a pod of Orcas launched a wolf pack assault on the *Osborne* creature and were yanking hard on its rear flippers and the hindmost portions of its body. This caused it to be pulled back and down, elevating its head and paddles above the surface as it fought to escape.

An Orca attacks a sea turtle. This demonstrates exactly what was witnessed during the Osborne incident. A huge turtle, attacked from below by several killer whales, would demonstrate this precise behavior.

Monster of the Deep

This testimonial was first published under the title "Monster of the Deep" in the April 27th, 1883 edition of the *New York Times*.[*]

---

* Source material: Andrew Hebda, *Sea Serpents and Other Creatures from Nova Scotia's History*.

"Captain Augustus G. Hall and the crew of the schooner Annie L. Hall vouch for the following: On March 30, while on the Grand Bank, in latitude 40 10', longitude 33, they discovered an immense live trunk turtle[1], which was at first thought to be a vessel bottom up. The schooner passed within twenty-five feet of the monster, and those on board had ample opportunity to estimate its dimensions by a comparison with the length of the schooner. The turtle was at least 40 feet long, 30 feet wide, and 30 feet from the apex of the back to the bottom of the under shell. The flippers were 20 feet long. It was not deemed advisable to attempt its capture."

Per the source material, although the coordinates appear to be in error, there was a Captain Augustus H. Hall at the time, commanding a halibut boat named the *Annie C. Hall* out of Gloucester. If one assumes the account has merit, with the neck being one-third of the overall length, it is possible that this was a large adult *Titanichelys*. Also, per the source, "trunk turtle" is the old-fashioned name for a leatherback turtle. With Liimatta's animal being described as "shell-less", this, too, appears to at least partially corroborate.

San Clemente Monster

In 1922, a young boy by the name of Howard Wilson and his mother Grace observed a creature that behaved a lot like the Liimatta turtle. The two watched in wonder from the window of their family's grocery store in Aliso Beach, California, as the head and neck of a huge sea creature rose up from the water.[*]

According to the family's description, the creature had black, glistening skin and held its head high out of the water as it moved along. At one point, it even turned in their general direction and blinked. Based on a sketch Howard did, it had

---

[*] http://www.light-headed.com/asite/laguna/laguna_history/south_laguna_1.php

61

forward-facing eyes, a blunt, almost equine face, and a pair of short horns on the back of its head.

He described it as being larger than a tree, with a flexible neck that dipped down toward the water (fishing, perhaps?) and then straightened up again. It moved under its own power, and the water around it churned as it propelled itself.

*Drawing of the creature by Howard Wilson.

This would not be the last time that what came to be known as the "Clemente Serpent" was spotted.

San Clemente island is about sixty miles offshore from Aliso Beach. During the 1920s a big game fisherman by the name of Ralph Bandini had two encounters with what sounds like the same creature the Wilsons saw. In an interview with *Tight Lines*[*] he said, "All of a sudden, I saw something dark and big heave up, a great columnar neck and head...lifting a good ten feet. It must have been five or six feet thick...But the eyes

* https://www.sandiegoreader.com/news/2010/jul/28/feature-i-just-saw-frightful-monster/

— those were what held me! — at least a foot in diameter, and dull and indifferent as those of a dying man."

Although he couldn't see the creature's body, he said, when a wave impacted on it, it didn't rise or fall. (this suggests it was using its flippers to hold position, something that the Liimatta creature can be seen doing). Bandini went on to say, "It was greater than the biggest whale." He also stated that it wasn't snake-like. "If it was, then we had better revise our views on serpents."

Several of Bandini's friends also saw the creature. Among them was George Farnsworth, then president of the popular *Avalon Tuna Club*. He stated: "Its eyes were twelve inches in diameter, not set on the side like an ordinary fish, but more central. It had a big mane of hair about two feet long." (this may have been seaweed)

He went on to say that, as his boat drew near, the beast vanished underwater without a trace. "This was no sea elephant. It was some kind of mammal, for it could not have been standing so long unless it was."

Ralph Bandini went on to write a book called, *Men, Fish and Tackle: The Story of J.A. Coxe as told by Ralph Bandini* (Coachwhip Publications, 1936). In it, he covered his friend J.A. Coxe's encounter with the San Clemente Serpent. Coxe's description was similar, with the creature having large eyes, a long neck that was five or six feet thick, and a reptilian head with red protrusions emanating from it. Its eyes were similar – expressionless and cold – and when approached it did what it did to George Farnsworth: it slipped beneath the waves without a ripple and vanished.

There are many more sightings of this animal in that region. Interestingly, once the Navy started using San Clemente for munitions testing and bombardment (bombs, depth charges, Polaris missile launches) in the 1960s the sightings stopped. Assuming the creature(s) weren't killed, they obviously had the sense to move on.

Vancouver Island take two?

An undated and, in my opinion, sadly lacking report from several cryptozoology sites[*] states that a Canadian fisherman by the name of George Zegers had an encounter with a sea monster off the coast of Vancouver Island: the same general place as Garry Liimatta. He described the feeling of being watched, then turned to see the head of a large creature protruding from the water about 150 feet from his boat. He said the animal's head had protruding black eyes that stared at him and a neck that was over six feet long (2+ meters).[**]

Based on description and location, and assuming the validity of the sighting, that *has* to have been the same animal or something very much like it.

Atlantic Sea Monster on the Loose

Per June 8th, 1956 edition of *The Troy Record*, a mega-turtle was spotted on June 6th, 1956 off Nova Scotia.[***]

Sea Monster Loose in Atlantic (Chatham Mass, A.P.)

"There's a new "sea monster" loose in the North Atlantic. The Liberian freighter Rhapsody, Wednesday, reported the presence of a 45-foot, white-spotted sea turtle in the ocean north of Nova Scotia. The coast Guard warned all navigation to be on the alert for the giant reptile which, said the Coast Guard, has 15-foot long flippers and can rise eight feet above the surface of the sea"

Both the size/proportions and color of the animal in question suggest an large adult *Titanichelys liimattii*.

---

* https://www.pravdareport.com/science/99220-whalessuicide/

** https://anomalien.com/whales-and-dolphins-commit-suicides-due-to-mysterious-sea-monsters/

*** Source material: Andrew Hebda, *Sea Serpents and Other Creatures from Nova Scotia's History.*

Pensacola Sea Monster

Certainly, the most horrifying incident, and potentially another example of *Titanichelys liimattii,* is the one that took place off Pensacola, Florida, in March of 1962. It represents not only a sea monster being sighted, but also details one actively feeding on human beings.

On March 26th of 1962, five teenage boys – Edward Brian McCleary, Eric Ruyle, Warren Felley, Larry Stuart Bill, and Bradford Rice – set out on a small inflatable raft from Pensacola, Florida. Their plan was to visit and dive the wreck of the *USS Massachusetts,* a late 19th century *Indiana*-class battleship that had been scuttled by the Navy in 1921 in the shallow waters off-shore, then used for target practice for coastal batteries and rail-way artillery. The wreck is permanently embedded in a sandbar and is partially above water. It is a breeding ground for many spe-cies of fish and makes for an intriguing, albeit hazardous, dive.

According to the article, *My Escape from a Sea Monster*, pub-lished by Edward McCleary in May of 1965 in *Fate Magazine*, it was "a perfect day for skindiving" when he and his friends started out. The weather was bright and calm with "not a cloud in the sky".

Before they got to their destination, however, a storm front moved it. The sky went dark, the wind picked up, and whitecaps began to form. The boys attempted to turn back to shore, but the outgoing tide dragged their raft mercilessly and they were unable to make headway, even with two of them rowing and two in the water, attempting to propel the boat via pushing and flutter-kicking.

(Note: it is possible that all that splashing drew the predator to them.)

Attempts to flag down a passing boat failed, as did their efforts to tie off to a buoy amid the rising waves. A heavy rain began to fall and the half-flooded raft was dragged past the *Massachusetts* and out to sea.

Eventually, the storm front passed, and the wind and rain went with it. A heavy fog rolled across the now-calm waters and there was an eerie silence. According to McCleary, "Not a wave rippled, not a fish broke the water, not a seagull called." Visibility was very limited and the water unnaturally warm.

One of the boys thought he heard a boat, then the stench of rotting fish washed over them. All of a sudden, there was a loud splash, and a big wave broke over the side of the boys' raft.

Just when things couldn't seem to get any creepier, there was another splash and a strange object appeared through the fog. Up and up it rose, until it towered ten feet above the surface of the water. To McCleary, it looked like a telephone pole with a bulb atop it.

As the teens watched in horror, the "object" began to bend, then sank beneath the surface. Everything went quiet, then a "high-pitched whine" pierced the fog. At this point panic set in. The boys donned their swim fins and dove overboard. All around them, the waster's surface was dotted with patches of crusty, brownish slime.

(Note: the "slime" may have been waterlogged scraps of rotting dermis, shed by the creature.)

Desperate to get away from whatever was stalking them, the frightened teens made for the wreck. McCleary and Ruyle were in the lead, with the remaining boys following in the fog. McCleary reported hearing splashing and hissing behind them. The fog began to dissipate, but the front returned and with it came the same gloominess, rain, and wave action they'd experienced before.

Suddenly, the air was split by a high-pitched scream. It dragged on for perhaps thirty seconds, then they heard Felley cry out, "It's got Brad!"

A moment later, his own cries were cut short.

Treading water, McCleary called out to his two friends but got no reply.

At this point, Bill had caught up to Ruyle and McCleary. With their number now reduced to three, they swam for all they were worth. Then, all at once, McCleary turned and realized Bill was gone.

He'd vanished without a trace.

A flash of lightning revealed the *Massachusetts* directly ahead, and the two remaining boys made for the wreck. McCleary reported that there was a second flash which revealed Ruyle ahead of him and closing on it.

Then, before McCleary's disbelieving eyes, the thing they'd seen before surface right beside Ruyle. He could see its eyes; there were two of them, and small. Then it opened its mouth and seized Ruyle, disappearing underwater with him in its jaws.

In a state of shock now, McCleary somehow managed to make it to shore. He had no recollection as to how he got there. The next thing he knew, he was in the Pensacola Naval Base hospital. He relayed his account to Naval Search and Rescue, but none of the other boys were found.

A week later, a body washed ashore. McCleary stated that, to the best of his knowledge, it was Brad Rice.

Sketch of the Pensacola Sea Serpent by Edward Brian McCleary, featured in Fate Magazine

This is one hell of a story. People may dismiss it out of hand or chalk it up to survivor's guilt or such, but that doesn't mean it didn't happen. I was unable to interview McCleary – sadly, he passed away in 2016. Thus, I can only comment on his account based on the information given.

The "telephone pole with eyes" part of the story is reminiscent of Garry Liimatta's creature (or something similar), although I would have expected the eyes to have been described as being larger and the neck (I'm assuming it was a neck) to have been thicker. If I reference McCleary's sketch, however, it does seem reptilian, possibly a plesiosaur or a long-necked turtle of sorts. I would imagine that, seen through the gloom, fog, and fear-enhanced eyes, an exact representation would be difficult at best. And it's possible Liimatta's turtle's neck wasn't fully extended. Anyone who's ever seen a snapping turtle can tell you how far their neck can stretch.

The creature's behavior does jibe with other accounts. The difference, however, is the attack. Assuming that the account is true, it would mean that *Titanichelys* is a confirmed man-eater. Without seeing the autopsy report of the poor boy whose body washed ashore, it's impossible to confirm this. However, I suppose that makes sense. The animal is huge, and porpoises, dolphins, and pinnipeds undoubtedly make up a large part of its diet. With a human being of similar mass, and several of them flailing around in the water right in front of it, I imagine it would not pass up on the opportunity. Which, of course, begs the question; Garry's turtle looking at him as a potential meal?

A final thought. Demetrius, the man who, along with two of his friends, observed that giant octopus off the coast of Sanibel Island, told me something about the Pensacola incident. After it happened, there were "rumors" that Naval forces from the Pensacola base went after this animal and killed it. If that is true, obviously no statement to that effect was ever issued.

God forbid, that people should know such things.

Demetrius's source was a friend's brother who was from the base and who, according to him, was not the type to gossip. Said individual did not believe in "sea monsters", so he took it to be factual.

I suppose it's possible. There are many stories of military teams being brought in to eliminate "problem" Sasquatches that have developed a habit of feeding on people. I imagine something like this would fall into the same category.

Artist's interpretation of a plesiosaur attacking a hapless boater.

Blyth and Ridgway sighting

A website excerpt related to the world-famous Blyth and Ridgway Atlantic crossing reads:

> *"The American explorers Bleat* (Blyth) *and Ridgeway* (Ridgway) *provided an account of their nighttime meeting with the Great Sea Serpent in July 1966. The explorers were rowing across the Atlantic. One night they were startled to see a large snakelike head emerging from the water. The head was attached to a long flexible neck. The creature's protruding eyes were the size of a saucer. There was a greenish twinkle in those eyes as they goggled at the humans. The creature swam parallel to the boat, fixing its eyes on the explorers. After overtaking the boat, the mysterious animal flashed its bulky body for a moment and dove underwater, leaving a fluorescent track on the surface of the ocean. According to the explorers, the monster scared the living daylights out of them. They felt like a couple of rabbits being watched by a constrictor. People can be struck with awe even if they happen to see the eyes of a sea serpent at a distance."*[*]

Although succinct, this once again sounds like the behavior of Liimatta's creature. Another report I read on the incident stated the animal was around 35 feet long, so the size is also appropriate. I like the notion of the animal tracking bioluminescent algae. It must've been something to see.

Fortune Bay sighting

A far more recent encounter that smacks of *Titanichelys liimattii* took place off the southern coast of Newfoundland, in May

---

[*] https://www.pravdareport.com/science/99220-whalessuicide/

of 1997. Charles Bungay and C. Clarke were fishing Fortune Bay when they spotted what they thought was a bunch of floating plastic garbage bags. Being conservation-minded, they headed over to the bags with the intention of removing them from the water. When they got to within fifty feet, however, they discovered the "bags" were actually the body of a huge sea creature, which stuck its head up out of the water and glared at them.

Per an interview that appeared in the May 6th edition of *The Telegram*, Bungay said, "It turned its head and looked right at us. All we could see was a neck six feet long, a head like a horse, but his dark eyes were on the front of his face . . . like a human."*

The creature stared at the two men, then submerged and vanished. They estimated its length at thirty to forty feet.

The size is right, and, again, we see similar behavior. The head popping up from the water. The dark eyes, the curiosity. And a sea turtle's eyes are towards the front of its face, as are the eyes of the animal in the Liimatta film.

---

* Source, *The Telegram*, May 6th, 1997

The Sakonnet Sea Monster

The most recent example of what may have been a juvenile or subadult example of *Titanichelys* was observed off Teddy's beach, in the Island Park portion of Portsmouth, Rhode Island.

On July 30th, 2002, a woman named Rachel Carney was swimming beyond the Danger sign during low tide, when she suddenly started screaming for help. According to her interview with the local Channel 12 news network, Carney felt something pass under her, then a huge head, the size and shape of a basketball, surfaced right beside her. It had a recessed lower jaw and was whitish underneath.

The creature submerged and began circling her, so closely that it brushed against her legs. Terrified, Carney swam for her life, all the while screaming for her fiancé, Dennis Vasconcellos.

Vasconcellos wasted no time. He leapt into the water, seized Carney by the backside, and tossed her as far from the creature as he could while shouting, "Swim! Don't turn around, no matter what you hear!"

Deprived of its original target, the creature started circling Vasconcellos. He could see how big it was – fifteen feet long and scaly. A moment later, its head breached the surface barely an arm's length away. He described its head like Carney had, the size of a basketball, if not bigger, with four-inch fangs in the lower and upper jaw, "plus layers (of fangs) inside". It was blackish on top, with scales atop its head, and whitish on the throat region. It uttered a hideous hissing sound and water sprayed from its mouth and nostrils, at which point Vasconcellos wisely retreated to dry land.

According to the news report, a friend of the couple, Joey Mailloux, may have inadvertently attracted the animal. Mailloux had a fresh injury on his left calf which, according to him, bled for ninety minutes, with him rinsing the open wound repeatedly in the water. Why he did this, I have no idea.

My kneejerk reaction to this is that the creature sounds like an oversized leatherback sea turtle. The color and head shape are accurate, and the "fangs" described, including "layers inside", sound like the sharp, rearward-pointing papillae that line the throats of leatherbacks and some other sea turtles.

The size is off, however. The biggest leatherbacks measured are just shy of ten feet in length. Based on a known specimen that had a LOA of 7.2 feet and a weight of 1,540 lbs.[*], a scaled-up fifteen-footer would weigh over six tons. Also, the head is too large, and the serpent-like motions he saw it make on the surface, coupled with its head rising up out of the water, sound more like the extended neck of one of Liimatta's turtles.

Lastly, leatherbacks aren't known to prey on mammals – their primary forage base is jellyfish – so the notion of one being attracted to human blood in the water and being aggressive about it suggests something other than a preternaturally large *Dermochelys coriacea*. It implies a species that preys on mammals and is opportunistic enough to view an injured *Homo sapiens* as food.

Sources

https://www.youtube.com/watch?v=myZB7DCXeO8

http://www.anchorrising.com/barnacles/004850.html?fbclid=IwARlpEFb IZkZVhU_6XNQL0qUeOnr_F7VNs9bB2x8w1Q4X5uRTpe9lyHcLTvs

---

[*] https://en.wikipedia.org/wiki/Leatherback_sea_turtle

Manmade Lake Monsters – When Aquarists Go Bad

Anyone who watches the news knows that Florida is slowly but steadily descending into the Jurassic Period. I'm not talking about a reversal of geologic time. I'm talking about the tropical reptiles and amphibians that are slowly but surely taking over the state. Marine toads, monitor lizards, Burmese pythons – even Anacondas and Nile crocodiles have been found in the wild.

These invasive species adapt well to the Floridian climate and proliferate unchecked. This has proven devastating to our indigenous species and is often dangerous to human beings as well. Personally, I find the thought of walking by a lake or river and having an eighteen-foot crocodile or thirty-foot snake lunging out and grabbing me or a member of my family to be far from comforting. But if these animals are not reined in, things could eventually get to that point.

Sadly, these invading armies are almost entirely the result of exotic pets either escaping from their enclosures or being deliberately released into the wild by irresponsible owners. Once freed, they survive and multiply, wreaking havoc on their environments. (A notable exception would be the marine toad, *Bufo marinus*, AKA the "cane toad", which was deliberately released into the wild in the hopes it would devour beetles that were destroying sugar cane crops.)

Encounters with escaped exotic pets are not limited to Florida, however. Back when I lived in the not-so-great state of New Jersey (sorry, I love the people, but the taxes suck, the CCP laws bite, and the fishing regulations are totalitarian), I used to fish a couple of local ponds, or lagoons, as I called them. They came in handy if I was pressed for time, too lazy to take the boat out, or doing some editing and wanted to wet a line or two while polishing a chapter. They tended to be small bodies of water – a few acres, give or take – but highly productive if one knew where and how to work them. There wasn't anything giant, but they had plenty of sunfish, keeper-size bass, and pickerel, although the largest fish consisted of carp and channel catfish.

One scalding July day, with the thermometer hovering around the 100-degree mark, I took my brother and nephew to one of these ponds. It was the little man's first fishing trip, and I wanted to make sure it would be productive.

When we pulled up in an adjacent parking lot, we found it to be a good 400-foot walk to the pond's edge, through a nearby field. We walked over to inspect the area, before committing to lugging our folding chairs and tackle there. When we got to the water's edge, I gave the area a quick once-over. Despite the oppressive heat, I had a feeling the fishing would be productive.

Before I could relay this to my brother, however, my eyes were drawn to a sudden commotion to my left. There, on the hot clay that bordered the pond, stood an enormous lizard. Annoyed by the sound of our voices, it had stopped sunning itself and rose grudgingly to its feet. With its massive belly dragging, it sauntered down to the water's edge and waded right in. A few strokes of its long, whip-like tail and it was gone.

I knew at once that it was some sort of monitor lizard. In fact, it resembled a Komodo dragon, which was obviously impossible. Still, I estimated its length at well over six feet, probably closer to seven.

I wondered if the oppressive heat was getting to me and turned to my brother. "Did you *see* that?" I asked. He wore a guarded look and, in typical lawyer fashion, replied, "See *what*? What did *you* see?" I shook my head and spouted, "A big %*%#~^ lizard!" "Yes!" he answered, obviously relieved that he wasn't the only lunatic standing there.

We then proceeded to discuss what it was. We knew that it wasn't any sort of crocodilian (based on its body shape, saunter, and tail design), and agreed it must've been a very large Nile or Water monitor. Presumably, it was someone's pet that had escaped recently, and now made a living on the unwary fish and fowl that inhabited its new home. It had to be; how else could a tropical reptile survive in a NJ pond that undoubtedly froze over every winter?

I suppose it's possible. I recall watching a special on alligators in the NYC sewers. Testing showed that, between the heat generated by decomposition and radiating from the buildings above, it stays relatively balmy down there, even in winter. There *was* a large storm drain that emptied into that pond. If that connected to the sewers, maybe said lizard spent its winters below ground, feeding on rats.

At any rate, undeterred by our saurian nemesis, we agreed to fish the spot. I don't know what he was thinking, but my brother told my nephew to wait there while we went back to the truck and got our gear (my nephew was too small to help, not to mention he had a cast on his leg at the time) I was aghast. "There's a giant, carnivorous lizard in that water, and you're going to leave your four-year-old son standing here, *alone*?" I spouted. He saw my point and took to lounging, while I made the obligatory two trips to cart our stuff over.

As it turned out, the fishing was good, which surprised me. I thought for sure that damn dragon would've cleaned the place out!

A giant monitor lizard, similar to the one encountered
by the author and family members.

Escaped Convicts

Somewhere in New Jersey (I'm not saying where, as I plan on
going back there and taking a stab at these behemoths myself)
there is a mid-size lake that is home to several lake "monsters"
in the form of exceptionally large tropical fish. These creatures
were undoubtedly once part of someone's home aquarium.
Eventually, they grew tired of caring for them or the fish grew
too big and they released them into this lake.

For the purpose of this book, we will call the lake *Jurassic*.
It's (among other things) the name of a deep hole I fished off
Cook Inlet, Alaska. The spot is known for producing hellaciously large Pacific halibut, so it's apropos for the place I'm
referring to.

Jurassic is a medium-sized lake and, like 90% of the lakes in
New Jersey, it's electric-only. That means no gas engines; trolling motors and oars only.

I discovered evidence of at least two species of gigantic fish in this same body of water. Based on my experiences and research, I firmly believe that both are members of an invasive species that originated in someone's fish tank.

The Body

Evidence of the first predator came in the form of a dead American shad that my dad and I found floating on the surface as we motored back to the dock. The shad was big – over sixteen inches long – and had a semi-circular bite taken out of it that measured almost five inches across (4.7 inches). It was definitely a bite; you could see individual tooth notches. The wound was instantly fatal. Yet, whatever disemboweled the hapless shad didn't come back to feed on it. It was more like a hit-and-run.

Sixteen-plus-inch American shad sporting a huge mystery bite.
Photo by the author.

At first, I thought it was a strike from a big muskie or pike, but that didn't jibe. The bite would've had to have come from the front of the attacking fish's "bill", and the teeth in the front of an Esox's jaws don't have the shearing ability to excise a clean chunk like that. They're more for gripping, like a wall of fish hooks. Also, the shape wasn't an exact match, and if just the tip of a muskie's mouth was almost five inches across, the fish would've been huge.

I focused on the bite mark and started comparing it to assorted species. A snapping turtle was contraindicated, as were our native catfish. I noted that the terminus of the maxilla/mandible wasn't a perfect semicircle or oval. It had a slight "peak" to it in the center. I considered the Bowfin (AKA mudfish, swamp trout, mud pike) as a potentially viable candidate. They're native, highly aggressive, carnivorous fish that have a mouth filled with sharp teeth.

Bowfin (*Amia calva*).
Image credit: Jeroen van Valkenburg, Monster Fish Taxidermy

As terrifying as the Bowfin's jaws are, the teeth seemed to be too narrow and tightly-packed for one to be responsible. There was also no indication of rake marks from the tiny teeth in the maxilla and, after watching dozens of videos where Bowfin devoured everything from fish to frogs to crayfish, I saw no indication of them biting big pieces out of their prey. Everything was seized and choked down intact. This is because their teeth are slightly recurved and are designed to pierce and hold, versus severing mouthfuls of flesh.

Lastly, the size seemed off. If a bowfin had disemboweled that shad, its head would've had to be six inches wide at a minimum, probably closer to eight. With the largest specimens only reaching forty-three inches and 21.5 lbs. it would take a fish double that size. Highly unlikely. *

The author and his daughter with a pair of Bowfins, prior to release.

---

* https://en.wikipedia.org/wiki/Bowfin

After a thorough investigation, I came upon what I believe to be the offending party. It is a large and notorious fish, invasive to this country, and infamous for taking over bodies of water where it's released. It can breathe air, survive for long periods of time out of water, and travel considerable distances on land by squirming its way along. It's one of the few fish that has a price on its head, i.e. "kill on sight", and has even appeared in several horror movies where it's been given the nickname "Fishzilla".

The snakehead.

A pair of snakeheads in the wild.

Channa argus, the Northern snakehead, and *Channa micropeltes*, the Giant snakehead, have both been found in the United States. All are originally believed to be the result of aquarium releases, and the Northern species (being capable of surviving colder waters) is known to have established breeding populations. The Giant, being tropical, has not. At least, as far as is known.

I believe the fish that destroyed that shad was a Snakehead. The bite is a spot-on match, both in terms of tooth separation and placement, as well as overall jaw shape. Moreover, snakeheads are fast and have exceptionally powerful jaws. They're notorious for attacking fish of large size – ones seemingly too big for them to feed on, like our native bass – and biting big chunks out of them. They've been filmed rocketing into a fish half their size, biting off its head or back half, and then circling back for more. Sometimes they even attack a school of prey fish and bounce from victim to victim like a pinball, taking fatal bites out of numerous fish, and leaving them to turn belly up, twitching as they bleed out and die.

This certainly fits the MO of the shad predation. After it was eviscerated it was ignored.

Convinced of the identity of the lake's mysterious "monster", I decided to calculate how big it was. In order to do that I gathered data on both the fish's head/jaw shape as well as body proportions, so that I was able to compare it to the (luckily) perfect shot I had of the actual bite.

Comparison of the bite mark to the jaws of a giant snakehead. Snakehead image credit: Monster Fish Taxidermy

With the bite mark having a maximum diameter of 4.8 inches, I took a dorsal image view of a snakehead and morphed it over the bite. I scaled up until I had a decent matchup for it. Although far from an exact science, as the image shows it is a near-perfect match. In terms of proportions, I ended up with an estimated head width (at the gill plates) of ~9 inches. A very large fish, for freshwater at least.

Matching that up to a full-body dorsal shot of a member of the snakehead genus, I came up with an approximate 1:7 head width to body length ratio, based on where the gill plates were measured in the reconstruction. That suggests the attacking fish had a total length of around 63 inches and a weight of approximately 60 pounds.

Dorsal view of a snakehead.

Dorsal view of a snakehead superimposed over
the bite mark for comparison.

If it's a northern, it dwarfs the known record of only 17 pounds, six oz. A giant is far more likely, as they're known to reach 4.9 feet and 44 pounds. Of course, the lake is in the northeast, and the water there gets quite cold in the winter. That would seem to suggest that a giant, being tropical, is contraindicated. However, the effect of warmwater effluents may be a factor. The fish may be able to survive, but could probably not reproduce (if there is more than one).

Thankfully.

That said, I am certain that someone living near *Jurassic* decided to deposit the contents of their fish tank into the lake. They probably figured it was preferable to returning them to the pet store, where they tend to offer a store credit of just pennies on the dollar (an insult to someone has spent years feeding and caring for a pet). Or maybe the owner thought they were being merciful by giving their former charges a spacious home and a chance at survival. Either way, they released a dangerous predator into an environment with virtually no natural enemies, and where only huge predatory fish like pike and muskellunge are immune to its attacks.

Lord only knows how many times that behemoth has been hooked and either spooled someone or bit through their line like it was spaghetti. But then, I imagine that occurrences like that are how many lake monster legends get started.

Thailand Terror

In the same lake where my dad and I found that shad, we came across something I can only describe as phenomenal. It was probably a few weeks after the shad incident, and we were working our way around the lake, live-lining shiners and such. I don't remember the exact date, but it was late summer and toward the evening, probably five or six PM. We were getting ready to putt-putt back to the dock on one of the trolling motors when it happened.

Ahead of us, maybe fifty feet away, I spotted a pair of disturbances in the water. I cruised us quietly over toward them and spotted twin boils of water caused by the passage of a pair of large fish, cruising beneath the surface. They looked like the swirls that appear on the surface when you're bobber fishing for bass and a big lunker hurtles up from the depths toward your shiner, displacing water as it approaches.

Except these were bigger.

We couldn't see the fish themselves; the water was murky, and they must've been four or five feet down. I figured they had to be big, as the water was churning over a large area as each one moved along. I deduced that we were most likely looking at a pair of really big carp, maybe forty-pounds or more, running parallel to one another.

I tried several times to get close enough to put a bait ahead of them, but the fish kept changing direction. As soon as my boat got within thirty feet of them, they would alter course and/or accelerate. With my lone trolling motor limiting my speed to a maximum of two or three miles per hour, I was unable to get any closer.

Still, I kept trying, playing a game of cat-and-mouse with the fish in the hopes they would slow or stop.

I began to realize that something was strange about these two fish. No matter which way they went, they stayed the same distance from each other, about six to seven feet. They never separated and, oddly enough, when they altered course, they remained equidistant. When making a turn to the right, the outside fish would swim faster than the inside one so it never lagged behind. It was as if there was a stick between them, or perhaps they were like the front tires on a car, always staying in the same plane.

I pointed this out to my dad. He pondered it, then licked his lips and said, "Max . . . what do you think the chances are that those disturbances are both parts of the same creature?"

MONSTERS & MARINE MYSTERIES

A chill went through me as I imagined the size of such an animal, but I shrugged it off. I thought it was ridiculous and, after activating my second trolling motor (the boat has them both fore and aft) I accelerated to top speed. My plan was to get between the two fish to cause them to scatter.

It didn't work. As I closed the distance the pair took off at an impressive speed, heading toward the deepest parts of the lake. In seconds, they were gone.

I thought long and hard about this occurrence. It was so odd and so unnatural for a pair of fish to behave like that. It wasn't until I'd figured out that *Jurassic* had one or more huge snake-head prowling its depths that I realized something. There was only one logical explanation for what we'd seen.

Whoever had dumped his or her snakehead(s) into the lake had kept something else in his fish tank. Something that grew to a far larger size.

A giant freshwater stingray.

It sounds insane but it makes perfect sense. In fact, it's the *only* thing that makes sense. What I'd interpreted as a pair of fish, so large that they caused the water to "boil" over them as they moved, was, in fact, the ray's wings. The oscillating movements at their edges is what was causing the turbulence. That was why the pair never separated, even when banking. It's also why it was able to accelerate so easily when I tried getting close to it.

According to Wikipedia, the giant freshwater stingray *Urogymnus polylepis* is normally found in Southeast Asia and Borneo. It can reach 16.4 feet in length, including the tail, and weigh up to 1,300 pounds. Call me crazy, but I know what we saw. And I am convinced that there is one living in *Jurassic*.

A stingray at rest. Propulsion is generated by the outer edges of the "wings", which creates a rippling effect, disturbing the water above and below the animal as it moves.

Determined to test my theory, I went back to *Jurassic* a few days later. I was alone (in hindsight, that was idiotic) and, along with my rods I had a fishing bow and arrow, rigged with 100-pound-test line. My plan was simple. I would work my way around the lake and, when I once again encountered distur-bances caused by the "pair of fish" I'd seen, I would shoot an arrow dead center between them.

If it slammed into something and I suddenly found myself doing an impromptu Nantucket sleigh ride across the lake, I'd know I was right.

Luckily for both myself and my quarry, our paths didn't cross that day. And I haven't been back since.

The more I think about it, the more astonishing it is. Assuming it's still alive – and since nothing ever showed up on the news about one being caught or its body washing up – there is a lake in this country that is home to a fish that weighs as much as a horse. I'm absolutely convinced of this. No fisherman hooking that thing with freshwater tackle would have a prayer of stopping it. In fact, knowing how stingrays tend to hunker down on the bottom once they're hooked, once it stopped moving, most people would assume they were hung up and just break off. I'm the only one who knows where this thing lives.

I think it's time to go back there.

But with backup this time.

Yuri Grisendi from *Catfish World* posing with
a giant freshwater stingray, prior to release.

SOUTH SIDE SEA MONSTER
(CAPE SABLE SERPENT)

The South Side Sea Monster (erroneously referred to as the "Cape Sable Serpent") is a huge and highly aggressive marine cryptid. Reports of the creature surfaced in July of 1976, when it made several appearances in the waters around Cape Sable Island, off the southern tip of Nova Scotia, Canada.

Before discussing details of the sightings, I would like to point out that previous descriptions of the South Side Sea Monster, as well as what actually transpired, are largely inaccurate. Whether this stemmed from erroneous reporting back in 1976, i.e. changes to the story to make it seem more exciting, or possibly even a deliberate attempt at spreading misinformation, is impossible to say.

Recently, I was privileged to do a two-hour video call with Rodney Ross of Cape Sable Island. Rodney and his father were among the group of fishermen that saw this animal up close, and he is the last living member of that group to do so. It is a rare thing to converse at length with someone who has experienced such a thing, and over the course of our conversation I got a ton of never before published details from Rodney.

That said, hold onto your hats, folks. Because the winds of change are about to blow.

The Sightings

The monster – and from the descriptions, this is one of those rare instances when said life form actually qualifies as such

– appeared three times over a five-day period, starting the day after our country's Bicentennial, July 4th, 1976. All appearances were in the same general area. All encounters were by veteran fishermen, who were in the process of plying their trade – in this case, cod fishing.

The first encounter was on Monday, July 5th, and involved Canadian fisherman Eisner Penney. The second happened on Wednesday, July 7th, with Keith Ross and his son, 24-year-old Rodney Ross. And the third encounter took place on Friday, July 9th, with fisherman Edgar Nickerson and his 15-year-old son Robert.

Rodney Ross (Keith's son, and the person I interviewed) has a fantastic memory and an eye for details. He thought it pertinent to mention that, in addition to all the witnesses/victims plying their trade when they had their encounters, all three of them had boats with green hulls. There were other people that fished the exact same area that had boats of assorted colors – some white, some brown, a few green – but none of them encountered the creature. He also pointed out that the sightings all took place two days apart, Monday-Wednesday-Friday, with no appearances on the days in between.

As an IGFA record-holding angler who has spent more time on the water than some marine biologists, information like this immediately strikes a chord. I suggested to Rodney that the delay between appearances might simply have been a matter of appetite. The creature's actions, as you are about to see, were most likely the result of hunger. It was probably feeding on large schools of cod and, once its belly was full, decided to settle back down onto the bottom or return to its lair and digest. Once its appetite recurred (presumably a 48-hour digestive process), it returned to its feeding grounds.

The green hull color pattern struck me as interesting. It is possible that that color, when viewed from afar, and depending on the creature's vision (we will touch on its eyes shortly) enabled Rodney and the other anglers' boats to blend in with the surrounding sea. This caused the creature to be temporarily oblivious to their presence. That makes sense, as Rodney and his dad watched it for a prolonged period of time before it noticed them.

And the moment it *did*, it attacked.

Fact Checking

As I mentioned above, and per the eyewitness's statement, previous accounts of the South Side Sea Monster are fraught with inaccuracies, exaggerations, and, in some instances, flat-out untruths. In an effort to set the record straight, I've listed the bulk of these errors below so that we can clear them up and start fresh.

- The creature was not and is not referred to as the "Cape Sable Sea Serpent" by either the locals or the people who encountered it. Rodney has no idea where that name came from; it was not a "serpent" in any sense of the word.
- Despite colorful stories of creepy night encounters, the attacks all took place during the day. None were at night, but rather, in the morning, post-dawn. This suggests that the animal does not see well in the dark and, despite its size, has to wait until dawn to hunt.
- Although there was some fog/mist on the water, it was not overly thick. Visibility was, per Rodney, eighty to one hundred yards. Combined with the fact that it was broad daylight, they were able to see the creature quite clearly, even from a distance.
- The creature did *not* have a head like a boar, nor did it have a head like a horse. That is pure fiction.
- The monster's eyes were not like those of a snail. There were no antenna-like stalks or projections protruding from its head and waving around. Details of the eyes are below.

- The body was not reptilian. There were no scales visible, per se. Nor did it have a snake-like body.
- The creature's body was not covered in "four gray-green body loops". Where this description came from is anyone's guess.
- There was no "fifteen-foot neck that was two feet thick". This appears to be a matter of misinterpretation. In reality, the thing had very little neck, but rather a towering, tapered head that started off narrow at the top like a traffic cone and grew hugely towards its mouth, until the thick neck region blended with its enormous body.
- There was no frill on the back, nor any visible fins. Given the fact that the dorsal portion of the body only broke the surface for a few seconds during the attack on the Rosses, it is possible that there were pectoral and pelvic fins like most fish have, but if so, they were not visible to the witness.
- The creature's tail was not segmented. Rather, it was like that of a gigantic fish, like a tarpon's, in fact.
- Last, but certainly not least, previously published drawings of the monster that have been published are, per Rodney, flat-out wrong. He and his father spent hours with an unidentified forensic artist who showed up unannounced at their home. They gave him a full description and, when he was done, said he'd recreated exactly what they'd seen. Yet, somehow, when the story broke the drawing that appeared in the papers was completely different. Why that happened is anyone's guess. But the cutesy, "Nessie-like" drawing circulated on the web is a nice piece of artwork, but it does not represent the South Side Sea Monster any more than a spotted moray eel does a goosefish (an apropos comparison).

Encounter #1 – July 5th, 1976

Accounts of Eisner Penney's encounter with the South Side Sea Monster are replete with inaccuracies. Per his description of the incident, as was related to Keith and Rodney Ross: on the morning of July 5th, Eisner was fishing off Cape Sable Island. Interestingly, his location was not far from where past sightings of the infamous Gloucester Sea Serpent have taken place.

The first thing Eisner spotted was the top of the creature's head, breaking the surface as it moved through the water. He thought it was a whale. But then more of it rose up, revealing its true nature, and it rushed his 32' boat. He told Rodney its head reminded him of the bottom of a 15-foot boat, starting off wide where it protruded from the water, and tapering to a thin prow that stood straight up. It had a huge mouth and, as it charged, he kicked his boat in gear and made a run for it.

Eisner Penney: "It kept coming out of the water. By the time it was near my boat it was a good fourteen-fifteen feet out of the water... As close as I let it, it was coming up to the stern and I opened her wide open."

Per what Eisner told Rodney and his father, the monster began to doggedly pursue him. It refused to give up, and was apparently intent on sinking his boat, eating him, or both. It chased him for a good three to four miles, and kept pace even at maximum throttle (his speed was 8 knots). Unable to shake it and desperate, Eisner motored into shoaled (shallower) water that was only 6-7 fathoms deep (36-42 feet).

At this point, the creature finally gave up and broke off the chase. He watched as it submerged and vanished.

Understandably shaken, Eisner told the details of his ordeal to a bunch of fishing buddies who, naturally, made fun of him. He became a bit of a laughing stock, but that ended two days later when Keith and Rodney Ross (two of the men who'd mocked Eisner) encountered the monster themselves while they were fishing.

Encounter #2 – July 7th, 1976

On the morning of July 7th, then 24-year-old Rodney Ross and his father, Keith, set out for what they hoped would be a productive day of cod fishing. The two men got up at 4 AM, caught their bait, and were set up and fishing by 6:30-7:00 AM. They were anchored a few miles off Pollock's Shoal (erroneously called Pollock's Ledge in some reports) in 25 fathoms of water (150 feet) and had 100 fathoms of anchor line out (600 feet). They were bait fishing, using hand lines with three hooks on each, with each hook baited with a fresh (dead) herring they'd caught a few hours earlier. A three-pound weight was at the end of each hand line, and was used to keep the bait at or near the bottom.

Per Rodney's interview, there was some fog/mist on the water, but nothing that obscured things like previous descriptions. In fact, visibility was good for 80-100 yards and the fishing was great. The men were getting bites every time their baits hit bottom. They had plenty of double-headers, and there were times when each man hauled up two or three fish at a time. They had between 400 and 500 pounds of cod in the boat when the creature arrived. I suspect the smell of bleeding bait and fish, not to mention all the thrashing from struggling cod, is what drew the beast to the boat.

Note: Rodney wanted it mentioned that, before the monster arrived, the fishing had been excellent. They were dragging up fish after fish and had a horde of pestering seabirds hovering over them like a screaming cloud. The tide started to shift, and shortly thereafter the birds disappeared and the bites abruptly stopped.

Then *it* appeared.

Rodney and his dad heard the creature before they saw it. He said the sound was reminiscent of wind blowing through the rigging of a big sailboat. We agreed that the noise was probably the sound of the water churning as it traveled.

Rodney spotted it first, at around 8 AM. He said the crown of its head protruded from the water as it moved along, like the top of a crocodile's head. You could see its eyes, but that was all. Keith Ross initially dismissed it as a large oceanic sunfish, figuring the object they saw traveling along was the fish's dorsal fin cutting the surface.

Soon, however, the creature was behind the boat, only 20-30 yards back (logically, it must have been attracted to the aforementioned stimuli and was probably working its way along, systematically ingesting huge mouthfuls of cod). They watched it swim for at least 15 mins, wondering what it was. It moved back and forth behind the boat, forty to sixty feet from the stern, and shifting in the current from one side to the other. Not once did it look at the boat. The eyes were visible atop the portion they could see and they were huge. Rodney estimated its eyes were 5-6 inches wide. They were red with no pupils, and had no apparent sockets but, rather, protruded or bulged out from its head, like the eyes of a sea horse.

Keith Ross: "I've never seen nothing like it in my life. It was like something out of this world. A very frightful thing. My son Rodney said it was like some kind of monster."

After 15-20 minutes, the creature finally noticed the boat and its occupants. It is possible it had run out of or scared away any remaining fish and, upon hearing a sound from the nearby boat, rose to investigate. Per Rodney, it turned toward the east (their direction) and looked right at him. A moment later, it rushed the boat.

Keith Ross: "It started coming at the boat and Rodney ran towards the cud. It didn't hit us, but it came within a couple feet of us... It had eyes as big around as saucers and bright red-looking. I mean, you could see the red in its eyes like they were bloodshot."

Rodney Ross: "It had its mouth wide open and there were two big tusks — I call them tusks — that hung down from its upper jaw. It passed astern of us, so close. And we could see its body, about forty or fifty feet long with grayish, snake-like look-ing skin, full of lumps or bumps and barnacles. And it appeared to us to have a fish's tail, an up-and-down tail, not flat like a whale's... I tell you, nothing like that was ever supposed to be in those waters."

The true size of the creature became apparent as it surfaced and its head rose from the water. Almost all of it had been hid-den beneath the waves. The head was stalk-like at the top and 2-3 feet thick, rapidly widening to 14-15 feet at the base. It was only 15' from the boat as it prepared to strike. Its mouth opened and it was huge – as wide as its body – with an incredible gape. Rodney said its opened jaws reached higher than his head, and were wide enough to swallow him and the back half of their 36' Cape-Island-style fishing boat.

Rodney: "I never seen crocodiles other than on television, but its head was sort of like that coming out of the water. Peaked at the top, with a big wide mouth. Its neck was full of things that looked like gigantic barnacles. Its eyes weren't in sockets, but popped out of the side of its head, and it had two tusks maybe two or three feet long and four inches or so around. It was a frightening thing to see."

When we discussed the creature's appearance in detail, Rodney told me that, besides the huge fangs or tusks it had hanging down from its upper jaw, its mouth had four rows of smaller teeth. They were sharp and shaped like those of a great white shark. Its teeth were pale in color, not bright white per se, but more a pale gray or dull ivory. The teeth were noticeably lighter than the thing's grayish-black body, and there were no teeth lining the inside of its mouth, like the sharp, tooth-like papillae that coat the throats of some species of sea turtle.

Note: for the record, I asked Rodney flat out. He told me that the creature they saw was definitely *not* a monstrous turtle of some kind. Nor was it a mechanical contrivance of some kind, like a submarine or movie prop.

Rodney couldn't tell if the creature had teeth in its lower jaw or not, as it was underwater. It was *not* a sea horse, nor horse-like in appearance, as has been reported. He did state that its eyes protruded *like* those of a sea horse, which may have been misinterpreted. Its body was wide and round, sort of like a barrel or ovoid, rather snakelike in texture, with the whole animal stretching 50-60 feet. Its skin was covered in many places, especially its throat, with big, white barnacles that were 6-7 inches across. Portions of exposed skin were not scaly or smooth, but instead craggy, like it was covered with coral or something. It never spouted, and at no time was there any indication of it inhaling or exhaling. Coupled with its fish-like appearance, the belief is that it had gills. Rodney stated several times that he got the distinct impression that the creature was deformed, like an ordinary animal mutated by radiation, possibly from the military dumping radioactive waste in that region.

As the monster attacked their boat, Keith Ross gunned the engine in an attempt to avoid being sunk. Rodney, who had fled forward, stated that he both heard and felt a low thump as the creature nicked their stern. Despite previous reports, the two men did *not* flee and watch it submerge as they rode off. If you recall, they were anchored up and fishing. What actually happened is, as Keith threw it into gear, the boat lurched powerfully forward with their anchor line under them (Rodney described it as "steaming up over their anchor line" which was, again, 600' long). They never actually lost anchorage, but rather, traveled far enough forward to avoid their attacker.

They observed the creature on the surface for a few seconds as it prepared to submerge, and at this point Rodney saw the entire dorsal portion of its enormous body, including a vertical (fish-style) caudal fin. He described its tail fin as being like that of a giant tarpon, but thicker.

Once the two men saw the monster had submerged (note: per Rodney, their boat was faster than Eisner's, which leads me to suspect that, after failing to chase down a slower boat, two days earlier, the creature knew better than to waste time and energy pursuing them) they held position for a bit, then let their boat drift back into the exact same spot where they'd just been.

The monster did not return. At least, not right away.

Rodney said he and his father stood there in shock, staring at the water and not speaking for what seemed like an hour. When they finally did speak, he turned to his father and said, "Dad, what the hell was that?'. He figured he'd only been fishing for four years, but his dad had been a fisherman his entire life and would have an explanation.

He didn't.

Stolid individuals that they were, the two men decided to resume fishing. Not surprisingly, there were no birds and no bites. Then, all of a sudden, they heard the telltale whooshing sound somewhere in the mist, indicating the creature had returned and was lurking nearby. Unwilling to chance their luck holding up a second time, they upped anchor and prepared to leave.

Just then, they picked up another boat on their radar and headed toward it. Ironically, it turned out to be Eisner Penney, the creature's first would-be victim. They pulled up alongside and told Eisner that, with his boat being smaller than theirs, he might want to head back in. Rodney told him, "If you seen what we just saw..."

Noticeably shaken, Eisner shook his head, "You don't have to tell me," he said. "I *know* what you saw. I saw it Monday." Without further ado, he grabbed his bait and gear, tossed it into the center of the boat and told them, "Let's go, I'll follow you in."

And with that, the three fishermen, wisely deciding that discretion was the better part of valor, "got outta Dodge" ASAP.

The South Side Sea Monster, based on the witness's description.
Drawing by the author.

Encounter #3 – July 9th, 1976

Exactly two days later, on Friday, July 9th, where was a third encounter with the monster. This time, the target was fisherman Edgar Nickerson, another of the individuals who made fun of Eisner Penney when he told people what he'd seen. Despite reports to the contrary, and per Rodney Ross, who knew Edgar personally, Edgar and his 15-year-old-son Robert did *not* hear the creature before it seeing it. This time the thing – possibly learning from its previous encounters, where each boat's occupants had managed to escape it – came straight up under the boat and surfaced behind them without any warning, leaving the two men no choice but to flee for their lives.

Edgar Nickerson: "It kept coming up. At first, I thought it was a whale and I kept kidding my boy that it was coming after him. I turned on my sounder. That usually scares whales away, but not this thing. It kept coming and coming. It was a horrible thing... I tell you, if there's a devil that was it."

fish terrorizes fishermen

If here's a devil,

THEY SAW IT — There's something strange swimming in the ocean a few miles from South Side, Cape Sable Island, and these four men have all seen it. Top to bottom: Keith Ross, Rodney Ross, Edgar Nickerson and Eisner Phinney. (Photos by Alain Meuse and Fred A. ...field).

Four of the five witnesses who survived the South Side Sea Monster in a local paper. Image provided by Rodney Ross and used with permission.

Aftermath

When Rodney Ross and his dad got back to shore, Rodney related their misadventure to two elderly fishermen: Weldon Cox and Seaton Nickerson (both deceased, the latter no relation to Edgar Nickerson – Nickerson is a common name on the island). The men told him that the same creature had been seen off the South side of the island back in the 1940s.

It is possible that sightings of the South Side Sea Monster go back even further than that. With his encounter forever burned into his brain, Rodney did quite a bit of research over the years, making a list of other possible sightings. His chart goes as follows:

Possible Otherworldly Origin?

Cape Sable is not alone when it comes to unusual occurrences. Shag Harbour, Nova Scotia is less than ten miles drive from Cape Sable, and closer to half that as the crow (or flying saucer) flies. Shag Harbour's biggest claim to fame is probably the Oct. 4, 1967, Shag Harbour UFO incident*. During this occurrence, a large, brightly lit, rectangular object was spotted by witnessed ranging from experienced airplane pilots to a large group of fishermen.

After suffering several visible-yet-silent explosions, one of which "faded to a blue cloud around the object", the craft either crashed or lowered itself (testimonies vary) into the waters of Shag Harbour. A large swathe of thick yellow foam was reported floating over the region where the craft had vanished by fishermen and rescue workers alike who, believing it was a large aircraft, frantically searched for survivors.

It turned out not a single aircraft on the eastern seaboard was reported missing, and the incident was listed as a UFO

---

* https://en.wikipedia.org/wiki/Shag_Harbour_UFO_incident

encounter. Investigations by civilian agencies, the military, and even Jacques Cousteau's grandchildren[*] have, per official reports at least, found nothing.

Between the yellow foam on the water and the subsequent appearance of the South Side Sea Monster, I can't help but wonder if the two might be related. Granted, nine years is a long time, but consider the possibilities. Could an extraterrestrial craft have come here and crash landed – perhaps from a world where the inhabitants are of marine origins instead of terrestrial? Could a spacecraft be filled with seawater instead of the oxygen-based atmosphere that we would need to survive? And, if so, could the inhabitants of said craft be creatures like the South Side Sea Monster and, after running out of food, be forced to hunt fish to survive? Or, could the creature have been a pet of one of the ship's inhabitants, perhaps one that escaped for a time before being reclaimed, like a lost dog?

All fantastical notions, to be sure, and perhaps they should be taken as such. But a few things are for certain. This "monster", for want of a better word, was huge, aggressive, and not at all concerned about being seen. It was also, despite being vaguely reminiscent of a gigantic goosefish, alien in terms of its anatomy. Lastly, it seemed to display intelligence, as its behavior changed with each subsequent encounter. It was as if it was changing its hunting strategy, in order to increase its chances of procuring the region's fishermen for what I can only imagine was a seafood lunch.

I think I need to go fishing off Cape Sable Island.

---

[*] https://globalnews.ca/news/4319302/ cousteau-family-members-shag-harbour/

THE 1918 PORT STEPHENS SHARK: WAS IT A MEGALODON?

In 1918, a group of lobstermen fishing out of Port Stephens, AU reported an encounter with what is, if true, potentially the largest shark ever seen. Described as being "ghostly white" in color and measuring anywhere from 115-300 feet in length, this historical sighting is one of the most often touted pieces of anecdotal evidence for the existence of an extant population of the extinct fifty-foot mackerel shark, *Carcharocles megalodon* (now known as *Otodus megalodon*).

Of course, the question remains: did these men actually encounter a living Megalodon?

The testimony from the actual sighting, recounted by Australian naturalist David Stead, is as follows:

"In the year 1918 I recorded the sensation that had been caused among the "outside" crayfish men at Port Stephens, when, for several days, they refused to go to sea to their regular fishing grounds in the vicinity of Broughton Island. The men had been at work on the fishing grounds, which lie in deep water, when an immense shark of almost unbelievable proportions put in an appearance, lifting pot after pot containing many crayfishes, and taking, as the men said, "pots, mooring lines and all". These crayfish pots, it should be mentioned, were about 3 feet 6 inches [1.06 m] in diameter and frequently contained from two to three dozen good-sized crayfish each weighing several pounds. The men were all unanimous that this shark was something the like of which they had never dreamed of. In company with the local Fisheries Inspector I questioned many of the men very closely and they all agreed as to the gigantic stature of the beast. But the lengths they gave were, on the whole, absurd. I mention them, however, as an indication of the state of mind which this unusual giant had thrown them into. And bear in mind that these were men who were used to the sea and all sorts of weather, and all sorts of sharks as well. One of the crew said the shark was "three hundred feet [90 m] long at least"! Others said it was as long as the wharf on which we stood, about 115 feet [35 m]! They affirmed that the water "boiled" over a large space when the fish swam past. They were all familiar with whales, which they had often seen passing at sea, but this was a vast shark. They had seen its terrible head which was "at least as long as the roof on the wharf shed at Nelson Bay." Impossible, of course! But these were prosaic and rather stolid men, not given to 'fish stories' nor even to talking about their catches. Further, they knew that the person they were talking to (myself) had heard all the fish stories years before! One of the things that impressed me was that they all agreed as to the ghostly whitish colour of the vast fish. The local Fisheries Inspector of the time, Mr. Paton, agreed with me that it must have been something really gigantic to put these experienced men into such a state of fear and panic."

Obviously, a shark measuring three hundred feet is preposterous. But in the grip of fear, and maybe a few beers, unknown creatures can grow within the confines of one's imagination. *Was* there a shark? Undoubtedly. Was it two hundred feet long, or even one hundred? Doubtful. However, it may have been sixty feet long or longer. But was it a *Megalodon*?

My theory on the Port Stephens Shark

A few years ago, I appeared on a Blog Talk Radio show program titled *Megalodon – Super Predator,* along with cryptozoologists Adam Davies, Scott Mardis, and Julie Rench. During the show, we presented evidence and discussed whether the Megalodon might still be alive.

While prepping for the show, and with the Port Stephens sighting slated to come up for discussion, I presented my theory that the shark wasn't a Megalodon at all. This was brought up as part of the discussion and, as promised, I explored it in detail. Based on my research, I believe the 1918 sighting was not only not a Megalodon, it wasn't a predatory shark at all.

It was a whale shark. And a damn big one.

If you look at the details of the story, once you sift past all the fervor it becomes apparent. The shark in question was *enormous*. We know that whale sharks grow to huge sizes, sometimes exceeding sixty feet, and there are unsubstantiated reports of them reaching seventy-five feet or more.[*]

Perhaps the largest reported whale shark sighting was relayed to me by my old shark captain, Phil Lewis, who ran a charter boat named the *Adios* out of Montauk, NY. Phil was an amazing shark fisherman, and one of the most stolid individuals I've ever known. During our trips together, he recounted many spectacular marine sightings to me, including one where he watched three adult great whites working together to corral a pod of speedy bluefin tuna.

His most spectacular story, however, was one where a whale shark, which he claimed was every bit of ninety feet in length, came up behind the *Adios* as they were putting out a chum slick, and tried mouthing the stern. When the behemoth persisted, Phil began to worry it would damage his beloved boat and, with no alternative, cranked up the diesels and abandoned their slick.

A pale-skinned whale shark sucking fish out of a trawler's net.

---

[*] https://en.wikipedia.org/wiki/Whale_shark#Size

I initially scoffed at this, but Phil told me quite calmly, (and a bit sternly) that he was dead serious.

He said, *"Max, I've been doing this for 70 years. The shark was right behind the transom, ten feet from where you're standing, and its head was every bit as wide as the beam of this boat. That's 17 feet."* I scratched my head, still not convinced, and made a joke about the shark thinking the *Adios* was a potential mate and trying to get romantic with it.

In retrospect, however, and having seen videos of whale sharks vacuuming fish out of trawler's nets, at least part of Phil's account makes sense.

The shark might have followed the oily chum slick the shark boat was putting out (usually frozen fish parts, blood and oil, oozing through holes in a perforated barrel as it thaws) and was looking for an easy meal. Ninety feet? Unlikely. But, in all fairness to Phil, when I measured a head seventeen feet wide against a whale shark in the eighty-five to ninety-foot range, proportionately, it came up accurate.

So, who knows? Maybe there was, or even *is*, a whale shark of that size out there.

That said, mass-wise, we know a whale shark is a potential candidate. Now, let's discuss the feeding behavior that was observed. The Port Stephens shark reportedly lifted up a string of crayfish (lobster) pots, 3.5' across and took them, one by one. Each one contained many lobsters. Does this sound like a macropredatory shark? Would a great white eat a lobster pot? I doubt it.

True, sharks are known to mouth things to see if they're edible, and are attracted at times to metal objects (boat props, for example). But an exploratory bite usually determines what is edible and what is not. I honestly can't picture any carnivorous shark scarfing down a series of unpalatable lobster pots – whether they've got crustaceans in them or not. I *can*, however, picture a whale shark doing this.

Whale sharks eat krill, and krill are tiny crustaceans. I would imagine that lobsters and krill taste and smell similarly. It wouldn't surprise me, therefore, that a hungry whale shark, faced with the prospect of a mouthful of caged lobsters, would ingest the cage too, mashing it up and spitting it out underwater, and keeping and ingesting the crushed crustaceans, whose fragmented bodies would easily slip through (or be suctioned out of) the mangled wire frames. This type of underwater feeding would certainly appear alarming, and the fishermen would have no idea that their destroyed cages ended up on the bottom, right under their boats. I mean, with them believing they were looking at a mega-shark in full feeding mode, it's not like they'd dive overboard to check.

Another thing I would point out is that, nowhere in the witness's statements, does it actually say that the shark *ate* the lobster pots. It says it lifted them up and took them, "pots, mooring lines and all". The whole ingesting part is simply us reading into it.

Think about it; lobster pots are on the seabed, not at the surface. It is eminently possible – even likely – that an adult whale shark was in the region and attracted to the smell of crustaceans. During its search for food, it became entangled in the lobster pots' mooring lines and dragged them and the pots they were connected to along with it.

To the frightened lobstermen, it may have looked like it was eating their catch. But in reality, it was probably just wrapped up and was (hopefully) able to lose the mooring lines shortly thereafter.

There are plenty of instances where whale sharks are seen with sections of anchor line or ghost nets wrapped around them. Some have carried these burdens for years. In the case of the Port Stephens incident, this is by far the most likely explanation.

Vertical shot of a whale shark suction-feeding on tuna spawn off Isla Mujeres, near Cancun in Mexico. It is likely that this type of feeding behavior is what the frightened lobstermen witnessed and misinterpreted to be a giant predatory shark. (image credit: Simon J. Pierce)

What about the color?

We've addressed size and behavior. What's left, of course, is the question of color. The Port Stephens shark was (purportedly) a ghostly white in color. Are there albino or leucistic whale sharks? Yes. They're rare, but they exist. I should think a sixty-foot (or larger) whale shark with paper-white skin, "sucking down lobster pot after lobster pot", while the owners watched, helplessly, would make for an astonishing sight. In fact, it would be terrifying. With its unusual color, the lobstermen probably never realized their shark was just a harmless plankton eater – if they were even familiar with the species. In their eyes, it was a gigantic monster, with a head the size of their boat, and an eight-foot dorsal fin sticking up out of the water, as it made off with their gear.

In summary, I think we can safely dismiss the 1918 account as having been what it was: a hungry, albino *Rhincodon typus* doing what all sharks do – being an opportunistic feeder. Does this mean that Megalodon doesn't still exist? As I said during the podcast, *no*. The odds are hugely against it, but if it *doesn't* still exist, there is something out there taking huge bites out of whales and whale sharks alike.

For the record, there are researchers who have publicly stated that they believe said behemoth is *not a* Megalodon, but rather a sub-species of great white that reaches lengths of 35-40 feet.

Is that possible? Based on the evidence I've collected, it is indeed. And it is something we will address later in this book.

MONSTER GROUPER

I've caught some impressive fish in my day, including a nine-foot Nurse shark in the 350 to 450-pound class, and a twelve-foot Blue shark that tipped the scales at an estimated 730 pounds. Both fish would've qualified as IGFA all-tackle world records (and would probably still hold the title), but being a soft-hearted conservationist, I decided to release them unharmed (my lower back, not so much).

Sure, having another world record with my name on it would've been great, but seeing the fish swim away and knowing they would still be out there was far more rewarding.

Both of those fish were sharks. As such, their skeletons were cartilaginous, AKA made of cartilage. The biggest *bony* fish I've landed thus far would have to be an irate Goliath grouper.

The Goliath grouper, AKA Jewfish (scientific name: *Epinephelus itajara*) is a massive saltwater fish, and a contender for the world's largest species of grouper. It is a reef-dwelling species that inhabits shallow coastal waters. In terms of size, the species is known to exceed eight feet in length and can weigh close to eight hundred pounds. Far larger specimens have been reported, although (thus far) not documented. I personally know a former submarine diver from the 50s who claims to have encountered fish that exceeded 1,200 pounds. And a former client of mine from my health club days told me he was jostled by one that had a body whose vertical height went from his neck to his ankles (meaning it was five feet thick).

The Goliath is one of my favorite fish to catch. When the mood is upon it, it hits like a freight train. It is a powerful ambush predator whose size and strength will test the mettle – and *metal*

– of both aspiring anglers and their tackle. I've had them snap steel fishhooks as thick as a pencil, break 400-pound-test mono, and smash "unbreakable" rods like they were nothing. Best of all, when one comes to the surface, it is an awe-inspiring sight.

When it comes to acquiring prey, Goliaths are ferocious and greedy, and have a reputation for attempting to consume anything that will fit into their oversized mouths. They devour lobsters, man-sized sharks, sea turtles, octopuses, and barracuda. There are even records of them attacking full-grown lemon sharks. They have mugged spearfishermen for their catches, stolen large fish from anglers' lines, and have attacked people on occasion as well.[*]

The author with a 400 lb. Goliath grouper, prior to releasing the fish.

Many times, I have heard people who've encountered Goliaths while diving brag about how "curious" they are. This is due to their tendency to swim right up to a diver as if they're studying them. In fact, they *are* studying them. But it's not out of curiosity. It's to see if you will fit in their mouth. And if they believe you might, they sometimes try.

A bite from a Goliath grouper is no joking matter. Although they may look like the mutated offspring of a largemouth bass and "Godzilla", there is no "lipping" these fish. They have strong jaws, lined with multiple rows of teeth that bear a marked resemblance to those of a tiger shark. As a result, they pack a murderous bite, as a former charter captain of mine can attest. He once showed me a scar on his forearm that went from his wrist to his elbow – a memento from where a 300-pounder bit him as he was attempting to remove the hook from its mouth. In one snap, it sheared his forearm flexors right off the bone (184 stitches, if memory serves).

His solution? He canceled his charter, of course. Then he wrapped his forearm in duct tape to hold it together (duct tape fixes everything, naturally) and called his wife so she could meet him at the dock and drive him to the ER. When he pulled his boat up, tied off, and showed her the wound she fainted on the spot.

Of course, it's not just the teeth that you have to be wary of. I generally practice catch-and-release fishing, but when it comes to Goliaths there's no choice; they're a protected species. Once, I was pushing a 6.5-foot specimen we had boated back toward the water so I could release it. Despite the fish's 400 pounds, it was relatively easy. I was on a flats boat, which means it was low to the water with no gunnels, and the deck was already lubricated with fish slime.

As I was sliding it along, the big grouper, seeing the water beckoning, began squirming in an S-pattern toward it. As it got to the very edge and was about to tumble in, it rewarded me for my kindness with a powerful tail slap to the knees that dropped me. I swear; it was like getting hit by a linebacker.

I had another one, probably the size of the one that bit my guide, punch a ¼" hole into my ankle with one of its sharp dorsal spines. The spine went deep – an inch on a guess – and the resultant wound bled profusely. Seconds later, it started spewing this viscous clear goo. I imagine it was my body's immune response to the hordes of bacteria coating the fish's neural spines.

The author with a 250 lb. Goliath grouper, prior to release.
The blood is the author's.

Most of my Goliath grouper fishing has taken place in Port Charlotte, Florida, around the pilings that stand near the abandoned phosphate docks. The fish like to lurk in the pilings, and when the tide is moving will wait at the edges, ready to rush out and annihilate anything that passes by.

The largest grouper I ever landed there was calculated (using length and girth formulas) at around 460 pounds, although I lost one right beside the boat that would have tipped the scales at 600 pounds easily. I remember the incident well. It was toward the end of the day, and we were using stingrays for bait (yes, they love to eat stingrays). Most of the rays were small, perhaps

20-30 pounds – the perfect size for catching 400-pound monsters. But we were out of the lively little ones and the only one we had left was a big dead one that weighed a good 70 pounds.

Unwilling to toss the whole thing out there, my intrepid guide (at that time, great hammerhead IGFA world record holder Bucky Dennis) sliced off a wing that weighed 20 pounds, slapped it on the hook, and tossed it over the side.

Bam.

I caught a 250-pound grouper.

He cut off the other wing and we tossed that down.

Bam.

I caught a 350-pound grouper.

At this point, all that was left was the body and tail of the ray. It was a nasty, 30-pound mass of raw meat that, on its flanks, looked like blood-soaked steak a foot thick. Hooking it through the eyes, we dropped it down.

I felt the hit almost immediately, but when we gunned the engine to pull it away from the pilings (throwing the engine in reverse is a necessity; otherwise the fish run inside and hang you up) it spat the bait.

I dropped it down again and jigged it by hand. In seconds, I felt the thrumming vibration that signified something had hit the bait. Again, we backed water to drag the fish out into the open. And, again, it spat the bait.

At this point, I told Bucky, "This fish has been hooked before. It knows the sound of a screaming outboard means trouble." I told him we needed to give it time to eat. He was opposed to the idea, but I was determined. Finally, we dropped the bait down again and, within moments, I felt the powerful tugs that told me it was attacking the hunk of stingray.

"*Wait . . .*" I cautioned my guide. "*Wait . . . and . . . now!*"

I set the hook hard, and Bucky gunned it in reverse, intent on dragging our pissed-off quarry away from its hiding place. It worked. After less than a minute, the biggest grouper I'd ever seen was hauled to the surface. Or rather, it *came* to the surface.

Willingly.

I could see it, ferociously smashing the bait again and again with its huge jaws. It must've thought its dinner was trying to escape and it was intent on crushing it.

I kid you not; that Goliath was eight feet long if it was an inch. It could've *eaten* an average-sized adult human female with no problem. It was as thick as a double refrigerator and had a head that looked like it was thirty inches across.

Sadly, it turned out the Jewfish wasn't actually hooked. It was simply so incensed that it wouldn't let go of its prospective meal. All of a sudden, it seemed to realize something was amiss. It turned on its side and gave me a look reminiscent of those intimidating stares Andre the Giant used to give people, back in the early days of WrestleMania. Given that the fish was even bigger than Andre, I stared at it, transfixed and unsure of what to do.

A moment later, it released its grip and, with a powerful thrust of its tail, it vanished into the murky water.

Mystery Monster

As large as that fish was, it is quite possible something even bigger inhabits that region. I don't know if it's a far larger Goliath, a big bull shark, or something else entirely.

All I know is I had an unpleasant encounter with it.

Ironically, it was the last time I fished those pilings. It was a two-day charter. The first day had been fruitful in terms of numbers, but size-wise it was disappointing. My spouse and I (yes, I used to drag her on fishing trips) had caught a half dozen grouper, but all of them except one were small. Mind you, for most people, a fish in the 40-70-pound range is big. But not when it comes to this species.

We did end up with one big fish, the 460-pounder I mentioned previously. It was a brutal battle, culminating with the fish wrecking my guide's custom-made, "indestructible" Goliath rod.

With all due respect, I blame the guide, not the engineer.

He had a habit of topping off the first 100 feet of line on his spool with 500-pound-test steel cable. This was to prevent getting cut off, but it was incredibly dangerous. You could lose a limb to that stuff if something went wrong.

Or worse.

One of the author's guides with an "indestructible" rod, wrecked by a huge grouper.

On the second day, things went the opposite way. The fishing was still productive, but now all the groupers were big, ranging from 250-350 pounds. I was using my guide's backup rod at this point; a big, beefy rod, designed to fight bluefin tuna while inserted into a gunnel's rod holder. Everything was going great until the last fish of the day.

I should preface that by saying, it wasn't the last fish of the day by choice.

I had just hooked another grouper and hauled it out from the pilings. I started working it toward the boat. It was a decent struggle, but I don't know how big it was.

I never got to see it.

The waters of Charlotte harbor are surprisingly shallow – around 20 feet. But around the pilings there are an array of holes. One nearest to us was 70 feet deep.

All of a sudden, my guide spotted a big sonar signature rushing up from that hole. It must've grabbed my grouper, because it seemed to quintuple in weight. I was yanked sideways and lost my footing, then crashed sideways into the boat's poling platform. I couldn't stop it. All I could do was hold on for dear life as the rod was pulled down like an upside-down letter "U".

It was astonishing.

I'm a strong guy, but I couldn't believe how powerful this fish was.

Just as I felt my grip on the tuna rod begin to go, there was a loud cracking sound. My giant tuna rod snapped like a twig and the steel cable on the spool started screaming off. There was no way to stop it. Even the overbuilt drag washers my guide had installed in the big Senator reel couldn't slow whatever was on the other end. In a second, it ripped all the steel line off, then broke the 400-pound-test monofilament backing that was crimped to it like it was sewing thread.

I stood there, wordlessly watching in disbelief as smoke spewed from my ruined reel. The only sounds were seabirds and the creaking of the boat as it swayed back and forth. Far below us, our attacker made good its escape, my grouper clamped tightly in its jaws.

What happened next truly punctuated things.

I don't know if you've ever bobber-fished for bass, but when a big bass charges up at a shiner suspended beneath a bobber, you will see the surface swirling as it approaches. This happened to us, except the disturbance was caused by the attacking fish's body and/or tail as it spun in the water and made good its escape. The resultant swirl was the size of my office (around fourteen feet across) and looked like it had been caused by an irate hippopotamus.

My guide shook his head and said with that Floridian accent of his, "Well, I don't know *what* that was! Must be one of them thousand-pounders people sometimes say they see, but nobody ever catches!"

Honestly, I have no idea *what* it was.

I don't know if it was a gigantic grouper like my guide said. Maybe it was. And maybe it was something a lot scarier. All I know is I do *not* recommend anyone swimming around the pilings in Charlotte harbor.

If you do, you just might come face to face with something you'll wish you hadn't.

The author with a tuna rod that was snapped in two by an enormous, unidentified fish.

MEGA SHARKS – THE EVIDENCE

NEPTUNE ISLANDS NIGHTMARE

Since we're working our way up the size ladder, the first of the "big four" on our mega-shark list is the smallest. Not that a fish the size of "Bruce", the man-eating monster from Peter Benchley's timeless classic, *Jaws*, would look little if you encountered it while sitting on a surfboard or snorkeling.

As with the rest of our monster sharks, and unlike many sightings that are entirely anecdotal in nature, there is actual physical evidence of the great white I refer to as the "Neptune Islands Nightmare". Said evidence consists of a photo of a huge bite mark, found on the head of a large female white shark known as "Matilda". Matilda and her wound were recently observed by Neptune Islands shark researchers from the *Rodney Fox Shark Great White Shark Expeditions*, and a photo of her by Andrew Fox – son of legendary white shark attack survivor and researcher, Rodney Fox – was published on social media on March 17th of 2020.

https://www.facebook.com/rodneyfoxsharkexpeditions/photos/great-white-kissthe-giant-mature-females-of-the-neptune-islands-are-among-the-la/10152603670091427/

After seeing Matilda's photo, I knew right away that it was no propeller strike; she'd been struck by another great white. I could also tell by the state of her partially healed wound that the strike had been fairly recent, and not something that (as detractors tend to say) "happened when she was young and the wound grew as she did". For the record, people who make statements like that usually know nothing about how sharks heal, but we'll explore that in another chapter.

Curious about the details of this massive bite, I reached out to the Fox people for details. I wanted to know how big the victim was so that I could get a rough estimate of the aggressor's size. Andrew Fox himself was kind enough to respond to my inquiry. He told me that the shark's name was Matilda and that she was a bulky, near-max female pushing eighteen feet. That would put her mass somewhere in the realm of four thousand pounds (two tons).

Andrew also told me that the shark in question has a "particularly large-looking head and jaw for her length" (this will come into play shortly) and that the bite was definitely from a very large white shark. He said that, based on the pale colors on the underside portion of the wound, the bite was up to a year old. Lastly, he pointed out that a bite like that was not typical of the mating scars usually seen on female great whites, where aggressive males bite down on their flanks and gill regions in an effort to immobilize them for copulation.

A diagram of Matilda's head and neck region showing her partly-healed bite is below.

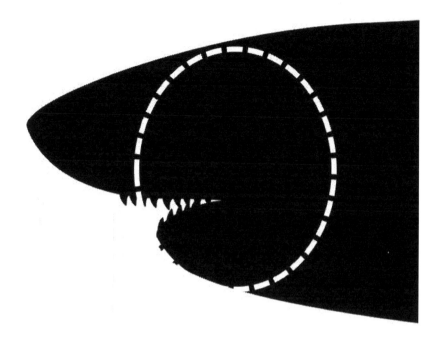

With this information at hand, I focused on estimating how big the shark was that attacked Matilda. And also, what caused the attack.

For the record, I believe that this was not an injury brought on by the "throes of passion" that take place during white shark mating. The reasons for this are:

1. As Andrew said, the bite location is highly unusual to be mating-based. Matilda was struck on the side of the face at an almost ninety-degree angle, like when one automobile "T-bones" another because someone ran a light or stop sign or failed to yield the right-of-way. This implies that the attacker either came at her deliberately from that angle (**A**), or that they were approaching one another head-on (or nearly so) and, while passing, the other shark suddenly lashed out, inflicting a horrific wound (**B**).

2. The wound appears to be exceptionally large – probably larger than Matilda's maximum bite gape. With the bite being fairly new, her being in the eighteen-foot range, and with female white sharks being around a third larger than males (adult males average eleven to thirteen feet, adult females fifteen to sixteen[*]), it seems unlikely that the aggressor was a male. He would have had to have been *enormous*.

The preponderance of evidence therefore suggests that Matilda was deliberately attacked by another large female. This makes sense. White sharks have a size-oriented pecking order when it comes to their own kind, with smaller sharks giving way to larger ones. Most of us have seen footage online where larger sharks have taken prey from smaller ones, and snapped at ones that refused to give ground (and divers, too!). A white shark bigger than Matilda would, perforce, be incredibly rare. As big as she is, she is undoubtedly used to other sharks giving way. She probably refused to give ground due to overconfidence or force of habit and, as a result, suffered the consequences.

The question remains then; if Matilda *was*, as it appears, attacked by a larger shark, just how big was it?

To get an idea, let's start with bite size. There are a number of ways to attempt to calculate body size in white sharks based on bite width. Sadly, none of them are foolproof, as there are variables that can throw a wrench in things. Allometry, i.e. body parts growing at different rates, can have a dramatic effect on calculations. Proportions in many animal species change as they reach adulthood. For example, it is a documented fact that, as bull sperm whales grow and age, their heads become proportionately larger, starting out at 25% of total length and eventually reaching as much as one-third. This has some bearing on sharks as well; Matilda, as we already know, had a larger head than normal. Yet with crocodiles, it's the opposite. As they age, their heads become proportionately smaller. For example, saltwater crocodiles typically have a head to total length ratio of 1:7. Yet Lolong, the record holder, had ratios of 1:8.8.

One option to look at is historical bite size. For that, we may consider veteran shark hunter and Fisheries Officer Colin Ostle, who was based at the Cheynes Beach Whaling Station (near Albany) from 1967-1974.* Mr. Ostle's job was to measure and

---

* http://museum.wa.gov.au/explore/blogs/glenn-moore/
whale-shark-lunch

take samples from whales that were brought in. In addition to that, he measured and recorded shark bites on whale carcasses. The largest bites he measured were on a sperm whale carcass. There were five that measured nineteen inches in width and twenty-four inches in height. (note: in 1968 larger bites were purportedly seen on a whale carcass but measurements were not taken[*])

Using the known bite size of a sixteen-foot white shark (4.87 meters) for reference and scaling up, it was estimated that the shark that left those bite marks measured twenty-five and one-half feet in length (7.8 meters). To put things in perspective, and using known weight ranges of 4,200-5,000 lbs. for a twenty-foot female, a white shark that size would tip the scales at anywhere from 8,700 to over 10,300 pounds (4.35 to 5.15 short tons).

Impressive numbers. But the calculations are not foolproof, however, as bite width tends to vary from specimen to specimen. A great white shark estimated at 19.5 feet (whose jaws were preserved by Dr. Gordon Hubble and licensed to the company Bone Clones®) had a bite width measured at the second lateral teeth (L2-L2) of 15.5 inches and a vertical bite height of 20 inches. Scaling up to the 19 x 24 inches bite marks measured by Ostle suggests his biggest shark measured between 23.4 and 23.9 feet in length.

Still another way is to go with formulas generated by elasmobranchologists. Research by *The ReefQuest Centre for Shark Research*[**] did both bite width and enamel height measurements and calculations on white shark bites inflicted on seal decoys. When struck, the flat decoys provided perfect bite impressions

---

* https://phys.org/news/2016-01-giant-monster-megalodon-sharks-lurking.html

** http://www.elasmo-research.org/education/white_shark/forensics.htm?fbclid=IwAR2QNb_CwOANMbynIr4e39DN54jwdcWOBg WFUuWSJCScFcbfPxfABmmJ3xQ

to work with. In this case, a bite diameter of 10.4 inches, coupled with a primary mandibular tooth crown height of 1.04 inches, resulted in a shark measuring approximately eleven feet in length (3.4 meters).

Based on these findings and scaling up, the size of the shark generated by Ostle's biggest shark bites tends to shrink. A nineteen-inch bite diameter now generates a shark only a smidgen over twenty feet in length – eminently possible, as we know such specimens exist today.

Last but not least, there is the formula that was featured in the paper, *Contribution of Forensic Analysis to Shark Profiling, Following Fatal Attacks on Humans* (Clua & Reid, 2017)[*]. This study not only helped identify the assorted species of sharks responsible for human deaths; it allowed forensicologists to calculate their size as well. Different formulas are presented for different species, which is highly useful, as there is considerable variance. It is also by far the most conservative method for estimating size.

Table 2 in the study stipulates that a white shark's length can be calculated by the following formula: TL = (BW + 2.4642) / 0.0986. TL = total length. BW = bite width. Based on this formula, Ostle's monster shark comes up with a total length of only 217.69 inches, or 18.14 feet. A common enough size for a great white, to be sure (note: with this formula the Hubbell shark, with its 15.5" bite diameter, shrinks to only 15.18 feet).

So, which of these is accurate? Based on allometry, it's impossible to say. Going forward, we will utilize all of these formulas, therefore increasing our chances at accuracy, while also being as conservative as possible.

---

[*] https://www.intechopen.com/books/post-mortem-examination-and-autopsy-current-issues-from-death-to-laboratory-analysis/contribution-of-forensic-analysis-to-shark-profiling-following-fatal-attacks-on-humans

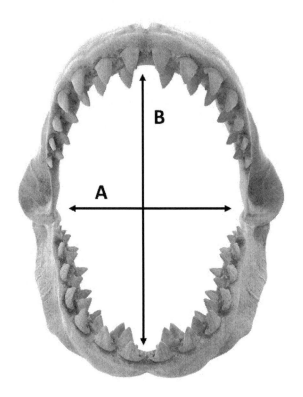

Shark jaw recreation demonstrating bite width versus height.
Ostle's largest measured bite on a sperm whale carcass had a bite
diameter that was 19 inches across (A) and a bite height of 24 inches high.
Based on the formulas in use at the time, that suggested a
great white measuring 25.5 feet in length.

With the aforementioned evidence in hand (evidence that
suggests the possible existence of great whites in the "Bruce"
size range), I attempted to calculate how big the "Neptune
Island Nightmare" would have to be to have a gape that allowed
it to nearly decapitate poor Matilda.

Using an anatomically accurate rendering of a great white
coming straight toward the "camera", I added markers to
show the contact points of the aggressor's jaws. I then took a

second rendering of a great white, also head-on, with its jaws at maximum gape and compared the position of its functional teeth to the points on the previous image. Because this type of test is innately rough, I kept things conservative. For example, I took into account that the attacker's teeth were already buried in Matilda's flesh. My penetration points therefore align with the aggressor's gumline instead of its tooth tips. In reality, it is likely that the attacker's jaws would have been capable of achieving a true bite height (gape) that was several inches higher.

Also, as Andrew Fox stated, Matilda has a larger-than-normal head, so when measuring head size, it's as if she was longer than eighteen feet. This implies then that her attacker's jaws had to be even larger, in order to encompass the entire left side of her face. By compensating for these two factors, we can be fairly sure that our estimates are "in the ballpark".

Based on this comparison, it is evident that a shark the same size as Matilda could not have inflicted such a bite. Without measuring the actual bite mark, it's impossible to be totally accurate. However, the aggressor had to be far larger. In fact, its proportions suggest that it was easily a third longer, putting it in the 25-foot-plus size range.

The conclusion? In my opinion, the Neptune Islands Nightmare is real. White sharks the size of the one that left those unmeasured giant bite marks on a whale carcass five decades ago may be rare, but they exist.

BEAST OF BRIER ISLAND

Next up on our "big four" is a massive shark I've christened "the Beast of Brier Island". Evidence of this shark is irrefutable, and consists of enormous bite marks found on the carcass of an adult humpback whale that drifted ashore on Brier Island, on or around, August 10th, 2018. This discovery is recent, and the odds are the shark that fed upon the whale is still alive and still out there.

For reference, Brier Island is an island in the Bay of Fundy, and is the westernmost portion of Nova Scotia. The island is sep-arated from Long Island by the narrow .31-mile Grand Passage, and measures 4.7 miles in length and 1.6 miles in width. It has a tiny population, and a large portion of its tourist dollars comes from, interestingly enough, whale watching.

The Bay of Fundy is known for extreme tidal ranges (forty-three feet), as well as being prime feeding habitat for a variety of whales. This includes finbacks, humpbacks, minkes, and the critically endangered North American right whale. Ship strikes are sadly common, and result in numerous cetacean deaths.

Of course, where there are dead whales there are sharks.

The humpback that drifted ashore that August was a large adult and was, according to researcher Jess Tudor, killed by a ship strike. Tudor, a native, manages Brier Island Lodge as well as *Welcome Aboard Whale Watching*. He works with many non-government agencies such as *Ocearch*, investigating whale entanglements, as well as the region's healthy population of great white sharks.

Brier Island researcher Jess Tudor taking measurements of a
Minke whale that washed ashore in February, 2018.

Tudor has seen plenty. But what he found upon examining
the carcass of the dead humpback left the Brier Island native at
a loss for words. The whale had been dead for some time and,

per force, its rotting remains were riddled with shark bites. But there were a series of bite marks that stood out from all the rest. They were the biggest he'd ever seen.

21-inch shark bite on a Brier Island humpback whale carcass, taken by Jess Tudor, August 2018.

21-inch shark bite on a Brier Island humpback whale carcass,
taken by Jess Tudor, August 2018.

Several of the bites had been inflicted on narrow portions of
the humpback's carcass that could be easily encompassed (flippers, flukes, etc.) and required no "gouging". As a result, they
could only be measured by width. There were several that were

a full twenty-one inches wide – two inches wider than the largest bite marks Colin Ostle measured – and one that stretched a solid *twenty-three* inches. This particular bite mark is incomplete – a portion is missing. The surrounding tissue was sheared away. If one follows the bite shape along its predetermined path to compensate, however, it strongly suggests that, if complete, this particular bite would have measured between twenty-four and twenty-five inches.

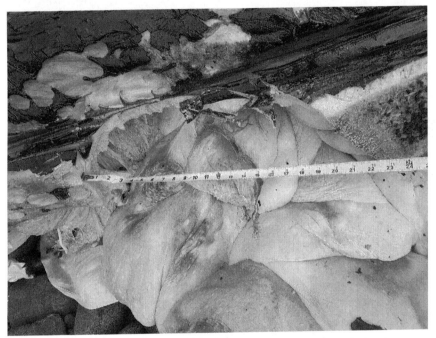

23-inch *incomplete* shark bite on a Brier Island humpback whale carcass, taken by Jess Tudor, August 2018.

Jess also managed to find several complete bites, inflicted on the dead humpback's intact flanks. The position of the carcass made for treacherous footing, but he was able to measure one on video, and it was an astounding thirty-one inches in height. Compare this to Ostle's biggest measured bite, which had a height of twenty-four inches, and it becomes obvious we are looking at a significantly larger animal.

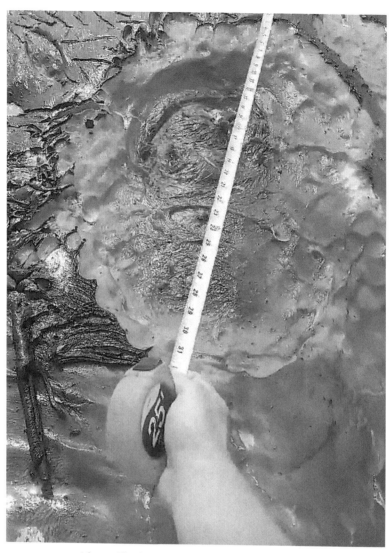

A video still of a white shark bite 31 inches high.
Image by Jess Tudor, used with permission.

The complete bite was definitely from a huge white shark; it has the characteristic oval shape the species is known for. White sharks are basically a larger, bulkier version of their cousin, and fellow mackerel shark, the Mako. Relative to their body size, their jaws are not as proportionately wide as those of, say, a tiger or bull shark, or the extinct *Otodus megalodon*. This is due to a stricture in the upper jaw. The third maxillary anterior tooth in the great white is smaller than the rest, resulting in a more pointed and hydrodynamic snout. This contributes to greater speed than can be achieved by a bull or tiger, but a proportionately slightly narrower bite.

Two gigantic white shark bites from a Brier island humpback. The top bite was taped at 31 inches. The bottom one is even larger. Photo by Jess Tudor.

I would be remiss if I didn't mention that one of the twenty-one-inch bite marks in the photos could, in my opinion, be from another species – in this case, an exceptionally large tiger shark. Tiger sharks' jaws have a characteristic shape to them and, as the set of *Galeocerdo cuvier* jaws below demonstrate, bear a marked similarity at least one of the documented bites. With tiger sharks having a wider bite relative to their body size than the great white does, and with papers documenting them at well over twenty-four feet in length, this is well within the realm of possibility. *

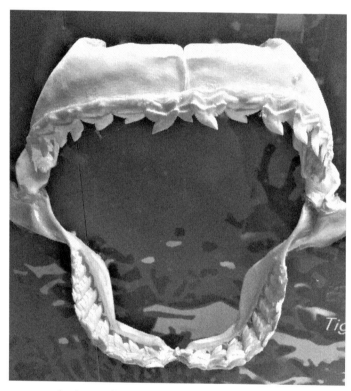

The jaws of the tiger shark, *Galeocerdo cuvier*,
showing their distinctive shape.

---

* *Simpfendorfer, C. A.; Goodreid, A. B.; McAuley, R. B. (2001). "Size, sex and geographic variation in the diet of the tiger shark, Galeocerdo cuvier, from Western Australian waters". Environmental Biology of Fishes.*

Using basic algebra, and comparing the thirty-one-inch bite on the Brier Island humpback to the nineteen-by-twenty-four-inch bites Ostle measured, I calculate the larger bite should have had a width in the range of around 24.5 inches. Interestingly, this is the size range I estimated the largest of the bites measured by width alone would have been if it had been complete. It is likely that this bite and the one below it (which was not measured but is obviously larger) were both inflicted by the same animal.

Next, I ran a tape measure on the screened images of the two bites, adjusting for angle, and did some extrapolating. The smaller top bite (which was tape-measured on video at 31 inches) is approximately 27 inches wide. This is broader than would be expected, based on Ostle's proportions.

Interestingly, the larger bite is 128% bigger in terms of height, suggesting a bite gape of around 39 inches. It is also comparatively narrower than the top bite in terms of width, closer to 27 inches. This suggests that both bites were indeed inflicted by the same animal. It also implies that, when taking the top bite, the shark did not hyperextend its jaws to maximum. Meaning, its mouth wasn't as far open when its teeth dug in. The odds are, at maximum gape, the largest shark feeding on the whale had a bite diameter of 27+ inches and a bite height of 39 inches.

We are now faced with arguable proof that there is a great white shark cruising around with a bite gape of at least 27 by 39 inches. Let's calculate how large this animal would be. Going by Ostle's calculations, by bite width (the smaller of the two numbers) it is a smidgen over 40% larger than Ostle's animal, which was calculated at 25.5 feet (7.8 meters). Scaled up, that suggests a shark measuring a gigantic 35.7 feet in length, or 10.9 meters.

That seems a bit large. If we go by the Hubble shark's jaws instead, which had a bite diameter of 15.5 inches and a bite height of 20 inches, we come up with a shark with a bite diameter 174% as big, and almost double the size in terms of bite height. Going with the lower number, if Hubble's shark was 19.5' long, that suggests the Beast of Brier Island was almost 34 feet long.

Next, let's incorporate the ReefQuest elasmobranchologists' formula. Going by bite diameter alone, and scaling up from an eleven-foot shark with a bite 10.4 inches across, a 27-inch bite suggests a shark 28.5 feet in length.

Last but not least, let's plug the numbers into Clua & Reid's formula. With a bite diameter of 27 inches we get a TL (total length) of 298.9 inches, or 24.9 feet. (Just for the sake of argument, I plugged in the numbers for the shark with the 24.5-inch jaws. It gave me a TL of 273.5 inches, or 22.79 feet.)

I'm inclined to go with these final calculations. They're more grounded (in reality, among other things). Of course, a white shark 25 feet in length would be an absolute giant – the size of an average bull Orca.

How is that possible? Gigantism is a pretty good possibility. Especially with known white shark size ranges so well documented. There are many instances of gigantism reported. For example, in the Southern Toad, *Bufo terrestris*, a female was collected that was 150 mm long (six inches). It was 33% longer than the *maximum* length ever recorded for the species, and 13.35 times the weight of an average adult Southern toad.[*] I once captured a *Scarites* ground beetle in Pennsylvania that measured a full two inches in length (51 mm). The species maximum is supposedly 30 mm. That said, a shark half again as long as they're supposed to get might be exceptionally rare, but it's definitely not outside the realm of possibility.

"Jaws 2" anyone?

Put another way, we are now in the size range of the extinct mega-toothed sharks *Otodus obliquus* and *Carcharocles auriculatus*. Again, basing its mass on known white shark ranges, such a behemoth would weigh in the realm of 8,007 to 9.533 pounds,

---

* https://www.researchgate.net/publication/254525332_Genetic_Verification_of_Possible_Gigantism_in_a_Southern_Toad_Bufo_terrestris

or around four to nearly five tons. With the largest known Orca taped at thirty-two feet and over ten tons, that sounds about right.

It also makes sense that a shark of such proportions would leave its calling card behind on whale carcasses. An elasmobranch that size would tend to acquire the lion's share of its caloric intake from carrion. Its swimming speed and maneuverability would be greatly reduced (remember, our 26.5' basking shark topped out at 12 mph), and it would find it very difficult to catch suitably sized whales for food, let alone fleet-flippered pinnipeds. If we're going to get photos or footage of the Beast of Brier Island, our best bet is to bait up – meaning to set up shop adjacent to a drifting whale carcass in that region, at an appropriate time of year, and play the waiting game.

Hell, if they give me a good boat and a well-trained crew, I'll not only do it; I'll bring the biggest, baddest rod and reel on the market and try to catch the overgrown SOB.

Anthony Corvino, a friend of the author's, posing with the head mount of a 17' white shark in Montauk, NY. The shark's jaws are approximately 15" across and the fish weighed 3,427 lbs.

PERTH CANYON COLOSSUS

Coming in at number three of our "big four", as we continue the countdown (or is it count *up*?) for our biggest, baddest mega sharks is the beast I refer to as the "Perth Canyon Colossus." Evidence of this shark's existence comes in the form of an immense bite scar, gracing the caudal peduncle of a pygmy blue whale, estimated to be between sixty-five and sixty-seven feet in length.

The amazing photos below come courtesy of Curt Jenner, AM for the Centre for Whale Research, which studies blue whales along the western coastline of Australia. It was taken in the region of the Perth Canyon, a submarine canyon that lies off the coast of Western Australia, at the edge of the continental shelf. The canyon ranges in depth from 2,300 to 13,100 feet and is a regular feeding ground for pygmy blue whales.

Of course, when it comes to describing these mammoth rorquals, the name "pygmy" is a bit of a misnomer. *Balaenoptera musculus brevicauda*, one of the three accepted sub-species of blue whale, is admittedly the smallest of the lot. Even so, it can reach seventy-nine feet in length and weigh as much as 143 tons – heavier than a "true" blue whale of equal length – with average adults being between sixty-eight and seventy-four feet.

At sixty-five to sixty-seven feet (20-21 meters), the pygmy blue photographed by Curt Jenner would be considered a young adult. And, judging by the attack it suffered, it was lucky to make it that far. The bite scar shown below is massive – estimated to be between thirty-nine and forty-seven inches in width (1-1.2 meters), and the wounds healed edges show telltale scars – toothmarks from an enormous shark.

How recent the bite was, and whether or not it "grew" as the whale did, is a matter of debate. I estimate the bite to be at least several years old. With pygmy blues maturing at ten years of age, and at an average length of sixty-three feet (19.2 meters), this particular specimen is at least that old. However, it is below the average size for mature males and females, especially the latter, and, as such, is most likely still a relatively young animal.[*]

A pygmy blue whale sporting a huge bite scar.
Courtesy of Curt Jenner AM, Centre for Whale Research.

A Pygmy blue whale sporting a huge bite scar.
Courtesy of Curt Jenner AM, Centre for Whale Research.

---

[*] https://en.wikipedia.org/wiki/Pygmy_blue_whale

The bite scar is interesting. A few years back, Curt Jenner was featured on one of the "Super Predator" television documentaries, wherein they explored the possibility of the mysterious shark eater being a thirty-five-foot great white shark "lurking in the Perth Canyon 'kill zone'".

On the documentary, Curt pointed out the presence of tooth rake marks still visible on the pygmy blue's bite scar, thus confirming it had been caused by a shark. He also noted that it was possible the bite was not a full lock-on, meaning that, when the attacking shark struck (probably coming at the whale from above, or striking it as it rose to spout), it wasn't able to get a full grip. The bite didn't attain maximum "reach". Whether this was a matter of timing, i.e. hitting a moving target, or the whale's caudal peduncle was too wide to allow for a full-on bite, the shark was unable to fully extend its jaws around its target.

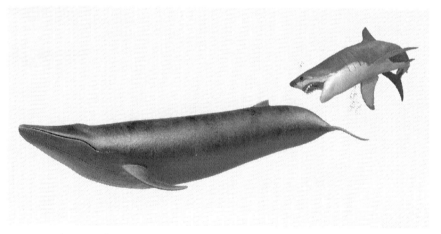

The "Perth Canyon Colossus" attacking a pygmy blue whale.
Image credit: Max Hawthorne (licensed images)

According to the documentary, the aggressor's gape could have been even wider than the bite scar itself, which is between three and one-half to four feet across (1-1.2 meters). If the shark had the time and/or been able to expand its jaws sufficiently, they estimated the bite mark may have been five feet across.

I examined several other photos that Curt provided me, and which give a perfect side view of the wound. I concur with the documentary's findings. The arc-shape of the wound is very wide and, if the rest of the attacking shark's jaws followed that same arc, it would have had to have been enormous.

Knowing the jaws of a white shark leave semi-circular bites (under optimal conditions) I took the image below and super-imposed a semi-circle on it. This was an effort to calculate how wide the attacking shark's jaws would have been if we follow the bite mark's arc outward. As you can see, the arc is a perfect match.

In this case, A = the bite scar (calculated at 1-1.2 meters, or between 39 and 47 inches). B = a dorsal view of the shark's jaws at maximum bite reach. C = bite diameter, based on what the completed bite would have looked like.

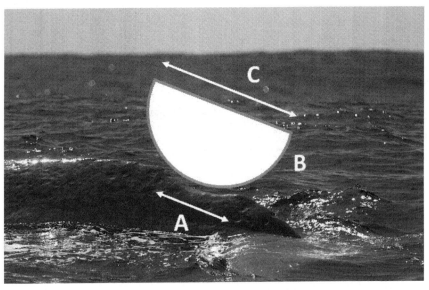

Pygmy blue whale sporting a huge bite scar.
Photo courtesy of Curt Jenner AM, Centre for Whale Research

There is an approximate 2-3.6 ratio between the bite scar and the original bite's maximal diameter (if the estimations are correct). That means the jaws were 1.8 times as wide as the bite that was actually inflicted. With the bite scar, again, estimated at between 1-1.2 meters, this suggests a bite diameter of between 1.8-2.16 meters, or 70+ to almost 85 inches. That's between roughly six and seven feet – a gigantic shark. But is that actually possible? Point of fact, no; that's bigger than a *Megalodon*'s bite diameter.

A great white shark exposing the jaws that leave behind its characteristic, arc-shaped bite marks.

Could there be another explanation?

In the interest of being conservative, and knowing that the whale was still somewhat youngish when photographed (the documentary was from 2017, and the original photo older still), I believe we may be looking at a scar that enlarged over the years. When I say "enlarged" I don't mean it grew uniformly, but instead changed shape. If you look at the preceding images, you can see that the current scar is fairly flattened out, with well-rounded edges. Whales don't heal like whale sharks, and a semicircular bite like that, located on top of the pygmy blue's sole mode of propulsion, would, per force, slowly flatten out over time as the whale healed and grew and swam. The continuous up-and-down movements of its flukes would have gradually pulled it open while the animal continued to grow beneath it. In my opinion, this gives the impression of a much broader mouth having inflicted the bite. The "tip of the sword" appears much larger, hence creating the illusion of a gargantuan predator.

Pygmy blue whale sporting a huge bite scar. Courtesy of Curt Jenner AM, Centre for Whale Research.

To test my hypothesis, I tried the same formula as before. But this time I went with the possibility that the bite scar had flattened out, resulting in its original arc being reduced. I inserted the same semi-circle, but reduced its size so that the "walls" of the substitute bite match the collapsed edges of the bite scar as it currently exists. One again, A = the bite scar (calculated at 1-1.2 meters, or between 39 and 47 inches). B = a dorsal view of the shark's jaws at maximum bite reach with overall size reduced to match the wound edges. C = bite diameter, based on what the completed bite would have looked like if the bite scar's original curvature had remained intact.

Pygmy blue whale sporting a huge bite scar. Courtesy of Curt Jenner AM, Centre for Whale Research

In reality, the original bite was probably quite a bit smaller, as was the whale when it was attacked. Most likely, the pygmy blue was probably still a calf, somewhere in the thirty to forty-five-foot range when it was assaulted by an ambitious predator. It may have been targeted when it was sleeping or while it was briefly unattended. Antarctic blue whales, AKA *Balaenoptera musculus*, wean their calves over a period of six to eight months, concluding when the offspring is around fifty-three feet in length (16 meters).* I believe this scenario is far more likely, as the peduncle wound would have been quite grievous and bled a lot. Besides blood loss, this would have attracted a horde of hungry sharks, and the youngster might well have perished were it not for the presence of a large and protective parent.

---

* https://en.wikipedia.org/wiki/Blue_whale#Reproduction_and_birth

The diagram below gives a visual depiction of how such a wound might have rounded out over time.

Artist's depiction of a peduncle bite wound elongating and flattening out over time as the whale grows. The original wound (A) is more semi-circular and as would be expected from a typical shark bite. The healed wound (B) illustrates how the wound depth may have stayed the same, but as the whale grew it spread out, appearing shallower over time. This change in the bite's perceived arc shape creates the illusion of having been caused by a much bigger set of jaws.

There's obviously no way to know with absolute certainty, but I'm fairly confident that the original bite's diameter was probably around 70% that of the existing bite scar. Does this make the Perth Canyon Colossus just a run-of-the-mill white shark?

Not at all. If I'm correct, we're still looking at an animal with a bite diameter between 27.3 and 33 inches (0.7-0.84 meters). Going with the most conservative of our calculation methods, and assuming it followed great white jaw proportions as relates to body size (allometric variations notwithstanding), it would have stretched somewhere between twenty-five to nearly thirty feet. That's a bit smaller than the documentary's size estimates, but still an enormous predator.

Definitely *not* something you'd want to encounter while free-diving.

And, of course, if we went with any of the other formulas, it could've been even bigger.

GALAPAGOS GIANT

Last but far from least, is the colossus I call the "Galápagos Giant." As the name suggests, evidence of its existence was gathered off the Galápagos Islands, and is in the form of a gargantuan "munch-mark", present on the flanks of an extremely large whale shark.

For those not familiar with the Galápagos, they are an archipelago 563 miles west of continental Ecuador. The islands are part of the *Republic of Ecuador* and they and their surrounding waters are part of the *Galápagos Marine Reserve*. They are known for a large number of unique species, as well as being the focal point for much of Charles Darwin's research. As expected, the reserve's bountiful waters are home to a spectacular variety of marine organisms, including sharks.

A diver swims beside a 40' whale shark. Note the 4' chunk missing from the animal's flank. Image credit: Simon J. Pierce.

In September of 2017 Dr. Simon J. Pierce, a Principal Scientist at the *Marine Megafauna Foundation*, was in the marine reserve and heading a research team from the Galapagos Whale Shark Project. While scuba diving, Dr. Pierce and Sofia Green, an intern at the project, encountered and photographed a very large cow whale shark measuring a full forty feet (12 meters) in length. As impressive as she was, what made the big female stand out even more was the even more impressive bite that had been taken from her left rear flank.

The bite was recently healed. Based on the photos taken, I estimate it to be approximately four feet in diameter (my estimate was confirmed via emails with Dr. Pierce).

And no, that was not a typo. The healed-over wound is a solid *forty-eight inches across.*

A 40-foot whale shark off the Galapagos Islands with a huge bite taken from its portside caudal keel. Image credit: Simon J. Pierce.

The implications for a bite of that size are disturbing. It suggests something seemingly impossible and, invariably, brings to mind a predator of prehistoric proportions, a la the extinct Miocene shark *Otodus megalodon.*

Before I delve into trying to identify the whale shark's attacker and estimating its potential size, let's explore the bite itself. The attack was apparently initiated from behind and, most likely, below, coming at the whale shark from somewhere between its three and five o'clock. White sharks are infamous for launching themselves at surface prey from below and doing their notorious "bite-and-spit" technique, wherein they crunch down on their target, deliver a devastating bite, then release it to avoid injury from a retaliatory strike (seals have sharp fangs). They then swim around in the immediate area, waiting for their victim to bleed out, at which point they move in to feed.

The 40-foot Galapagos whale shark with a diver for size comparison. Note the wound. Image credit: Simon J. Pierce.

This technique works well for the great white. When attacking large and potentially dangerous prey such as elephant seals (which may be even larger than the shark) the tendency is to attack the pinniped's vulnerable haunches. This greatly reduces the shark's chances of suffering a debilitating injury and, if successful, enables it to immobilize the elephant seal, eliminating its ability to swim to safety.

We see this technique used regularly by predators on both land and sea when forced to tackle formidable prey. It's not just a matter of size. Sperm whales, for example, have powerful jaws and, if attacked head-on, can deliver a crushing bite. And even baleen whales can fight back with blows from their boat-sized flukes or, in the case of the humpback, their enormous pectoral fins.

In the case of our whale shark, it was huge. And huge usually means dangerous, even with something as docile as a whale shark. The attack was precise and targeted a region of the peduncle far enough from the shark's towering caudal fin to reduce the chances of being struck, but close enough that, if successful, it would disable the prey item.

Whale sharks are what are known as obligate ram breathers and are incapable of buccal pumping. That means they must swim continuously to keep seawater flowing over their gills. If deprived of its sole means of locomotion, the crippled shark would have suffocated, providing a tremendous bounty for its attacker. Whale sharks are ponderous and tremendously slow, with a swimming speed of only three mph (5 km). So how did the attack fail?

The Galapagos giant's victim. Note the sheer mass of the whale shark.
Image credit: Sofia Green

Once again, the larger a shark gets the slower it gets. The whale shark's attacker was presumably a bit faster than it was, but probably not significantly. I think the victim escaped because of the region that was targeted. Whale sharks have the thickest skin of any shark, and in the case of an individual this size, probably up to six inches (150 mm). As I've pointed out in my abovementioned blog post, they also have an overly developed caudal keel – a lateral ridge on the caudal peduncle, located directly in front of and on either side of the caudal (tail) fin.

The whale shark's caudal keel is extremely long and well developed, running roughly half the length of its body. In addition to strengthening the region, I believe it evolved for defensive purposes. It acts as a sort of "crumple zone" or blister hull, and helps the otherwise defenseless plankton feeder absorb strikes from macropredatory sharks that might otherwise incapacitate or kill it.

In this instance, I believe the attacker launched itself at the whale shark and bit down, shearing away a huge gob of tissue in the process. Unfortunately for the aggressor, what it came away with was mainly tough and unpalatable skin, with the huge locomotory muscles and vital organs underneath being largely spared. The aggressor may have even received a stunning smack from the whale shark's massive tail – a blow powerful enough to rattle its brain and convince it that the distasteful thing it assaulted was not worth any additional effort.

*https://www.kronosrising.com/great-white-predation-on-whale-sharks-how-does-the-gentle-giant-survive/

A whale shark seen from the side, showing the elongated caudal keel.

Dorsal view of a whale shark showing its elongated and
well-developed protective caudal keel.

The question that remains is, how large was the attacking shark, and is there any way to determine *what* it was?

Before we can answer those questions, we must assess the bite itself. Naysayers and conservative types will be quick to suggest that the whale shark was attacked when it was younger and that the bite simply "grew over time", creating the illusion of a "super predator." In truth, as we've seen from our previous examples, even a white shark bite half that size would suggest an animal somewhere in the twenty-two-foot range.

But was the bite really that old? Is there any way to tell?

The answers lie in whale shark biology. Sharks in general are known for being phenomenal healers, and the whale shark is no exception. After examining closeups of the bite, I believe that it is not decades old or even years old. If you refer to the blog post on my website titled, *Great White Predation on Whale Sharks – How Does the Gentle Giant Survive?* you will see an example of just how miraculous the planktivorous shark's powers of regeneration are.

On the post there are photographs of a sub-adult whale shark (I believe it was around twenty feet in length) that suffered a ferocious attack from a macropredatory shark – most likely a great white or tiger. The first photo is from April of 2003 and shows horrific bites taken from the whale shark's dorsal fin and, interestingly, its caudal keel region. Again, despite the savagery of the assault, the harmless whale shark somehow managed to escape.

The second photo is from fourteen months later, at which point both bite marks are no longer recognizable. They are almost completely filled in and look nothing like how they started out. Their edges are now smooth and rounded, and skin has grown back over much of the area, even on the peduncle bite. All this in a period of fourteen months.

With this as a reference, when we compare the bite mark on the much larger Galapagos specimen, we can see that much less healing has taken place. In fact, if you look at a closeup of the right side of the bite, you can see individual tooth marks are still visible. They are long, deep, and very triangular. If the wound was as old as the one shown on my blog, the odds are those tooth gouges would be filled in. This leads me to surmise that the bite is probably less than a year old, with the already mature shark having grown very little during that time period.

Closeup of the bite mark on a 40' whale shark. Note the individual tooth marks. Image credit: Simon J. Pierce.

Another interesting thing about the bite is that it is not oval-shaped from top to bottom, like the confirmed great white bites inflicted by the Beast of Brier Island. Rather, it is more circular, almost like what one would expect from some Brobdingnagian bull shark.

Of course, bull sharks don't get big enough to take desk-sized hunks out of a whale shark the size of an adult gray whale. So, what was it?

Personally, I don't believe that the bite was the result of a failed attack from some preternaturally large white shark. Don't get me wrong; there are theories that there is a sub-species of great white out there that grows that large, or that the "mega shark" is the result of a genetic fluke, a mutation, i.e. gigantism. It's possible, but in this case the shark's jaws would have had to change shape as well. Unless, of course, it didn't achieve full bite height before it locked on. That is, of course, possible.

Based on the most conservative formula we've used, based on known *Carcharodon carcharias* bite gapes, a forty-eight-inch-wide mouth suggests a great white 42.6 feet in length. That's *enormous*. If went by the Hubbell specimen, it would be sixty feet long, and if we relied on Ostle's measurements, etc., it would stretch to almost sixty-five.

Highly unlikely.

If a super white shark is contraindicated, our next step is to consider what known predatory sharks have a more circular bite that is proportionately larger than that of a great white, yet also grow to enormous size. That brings us back to *Otodus megalodon* or something similar. We know that Megalodon grew to a maximum length of around fifty feet, so could it be our culprit? Could a relic population of the largest mega-toothed shark of all time still be with us?

Again, highly unlikely. But then, in the world of cryptozoology, anything is possible. Still, I tend to think not. Megalodon had jaws that, in a maximum-sized adult, could span five feet or more across. And the shape is, in my opinion, right for the bite. However, the largest Megalodon teeth had more rounded and robust crowns and were not as sharp at the tips. They would leave wider tooth gouges than we're seeing on our whale shark.

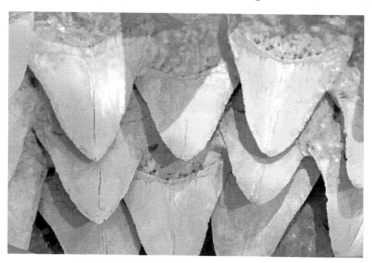

Casts of the bone-crunching primary anterior teeth of
an adult Megalodon shark.

Another possibility, although, again, an admitted longshot, is a species of extinct shark known as *Otodus chubutensis*. This shark is listed as the direct ancestor of Megalodon. In fact, most paleontologists believe the two split off from one another somewhere between twenty-eight and sixteen million years ago. This makes Chubutensis a morpho-species. During the Miocene and Pliocene epochs, the two sharks shared the same oceans for millions of years, with Chubutensis disappearing around five million years ago, and Megalodon vanishing around 3.6 million years ago.

Chubutensis was a huge predatory shark, estimated to have reached forty feet in length.[*] It had teeth similar to those of Megalodon, albeit with slenderer, more blade-like crowns. This suggests it remained an active predator for more of its life than did its larger, chisel-toothed cousin. Below is an example of a spectacular, near-maximum size Chubutensis tooth from my personal collection compared to a Megalodon tooth. As you can see, the tooth is triangular and sharp and lacks the more cylindrical, almost column-like crown core present in the primary anterior teeth of Megalodon. In fact, it is similar to that of a gigantic white shark.

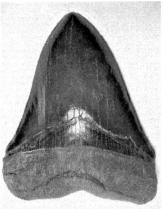

A pristine 4.75" *Otodus chubutensis* and 6.5" *Otodus megalodon* tooth, from the authors collection.

---

[*] https://en.wikipedia.org/wiki/Carcharocles_chubutensis

There have been numerous reports over the years of encounters with enormous predatory sharks. Could a small population of *O. chubutensis* or *O. megalodon* remain undetected, eking out a living somewhere far out at sea? It seems unlikely, yet we have evidence that such a creature (or something very much like it) exists. Seen from above, from a boat or helicopter, a sub-adult of one of these creatures could easily be mistaken for a large *Carcharodon carcharias*, and even an adult could be dismissed as a basking shark. Of course, huge adults would be exceptionally rare to begin with.

Speaking of adults, let's take a moment to estimate the size of the shark that gouged several hundred pounds of flesh from our hapless whale shark.

I'm going to base my calculations on a bite diameter of forty-eight inches. With a gape height of approximately forty-eight inches – double the height of the biggest bites Colin Ostle was able to accurately measure (note, there were other, larger bites on whale carcasses that he observed, but they were not accurately measured) the possibilities are frightening.

Is there a bus-sized macropredatory shark still roaming Earth's oceans?

If we once again went by our most conservative method of calculating white shark length via bite diameter, we'd be looking at a forty-two-plus-foot animal (every other comparison ends up at sixty feet or more, which seems highly improbable).

A forty-foot shark means a predator in the same size range as the whale shark it hunted. At double the length of a twenty-foot white shark, it would be eight times the mass. That means a weight somewhere in the range of eighteen to twenty short tons, or between 36,000 and 40,000 pounds.

Again, the speed and stamina of a predatory shark that size would be questionable, especially when compared to a sleek and agile white shark in the fifteen-foot range. This probably contributed to the whale shark escaping. Orcas, on the other hand, would have promptly torn it to pieces (yes, killer whales do feed on whale sharks).

In summation, the bite mark on that whale shark didn't get there by itself. It was put there by something very big and very hungry. And, since the photos were taken only a few years ago, the odds are that said hungry unknown is probably still with us.

You're gonna need a bigger shark cage.

The "Galapagos Giant" attacks the caudal keel region and abdomen of a similar-sized whale shark.

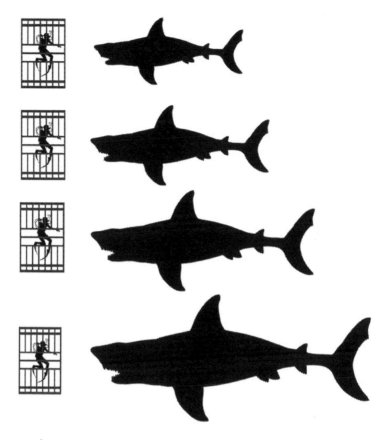

Diagram demonstrating potential "mega shark" sizes. A: a 20' great white, a la "Deep Blue". B: the 25' Neptune Islands Nightmare and similar-sized' Beast of Brier Island. C: the 30' Perth Canyon Colossus and D: the 40' Galapagos Giant.

Jaw comparison estimates of A: "Deep Blue", B: *Neptune Islands Nightmare & Beast of Brier Island*, C: *Perth Canyon Colossus*, D: *Galapagos Giant*

HONORABLE MENTION: IS THIS MEGALODON?

I would be remiss in my duties if did not mention that I have, in my records, a photo that implies the existence of a behemoth even larger than the above-mentioned super sharks. Unfortunately, I don't know who sent it to me or where or when it was taken. Nor have I been able to find it via Internet searches. As a result, I could not acquire the necessary release form and an unable to feature it here.

Note: this is not a hoax or "publicity stunt". That is not my style.

I will inquire about the possibility of utilizing the photo in a blog post. As it would be for educational purposes, under "fair use" it may be possible. I hope so. It would be a shame to leave it out.

In the interim, and for reasons that will become readily apparent, I am naming this potential monster of monsters the "Humpback Horror".

The photo in question shows a pair of humpback whales at the surface. They're either frolicking or preparing to sound. The only part of them we can see is their tails. Their flukes and caudal peduncles are both held vertically above the surface, with their bodies in a downward position.

The shocking part about the image is that one of the humpbacks has what appears to be an arc-shaped bite mark gracing one of its flukes. The damage – and it is almost certainly a bite, there are notches from individual teeth and ragged hunks of skin hanging – appears to have been a grazing strike. The attacker must have tried to seize the whale by its flukes and managed to chomp down on the underside of one, tearing away skin and a bit of flesh in the process.

Whether the humpback swatted the slower, less agile shark with its flukes or simply dodged it is impossible to say. But the calling card the aggressor left behind is not just unmistakable, it is astounding. If the humpbacks pictured are adults, that means they have an average fluke span of twelve feet. The bite mark spans one fluke entirely, stretching from tip to center. This suggests a bite span of six feet.

Imagine? *Six feet.*

Now, to be clear, there are a lot of "ifs" here. *If* it is a bite, and *if* it is a shark bite, and *if* the whales are adults. If all those parameters are met, we could be looking at something extraordinary. Frankly, I've never seen an image where a ship's propeller or prop strike left a wound like that. Nor have I seen one that left what look like notched tooth marks. And the shreds of tissue hanging from the wound suggest that it was fairly recent, i.e. only weeks or months old.

That said, I'm 99% sure it's a shark bite, and the law of averages, as well as species behavior, suggests that the humpbacks are schooling adults. They could be playing or they may be preparing to dive and herd schools of herring in a pod formation. Honestly, even if the injured animal is a sub-adult with eight to ten-foot flukes, we'd still be looking at a giant shark – something along the lines of the Galapagos giant. That is most likely the case.

Of course, if it *is* an adult whale, then the photo provides powerful evidence for the existence of a true mega-shark – one with jaws six-feet wide. To be fair, the only one I know of that can reach that size is everyone's favorite.

Megalodon.

Diagram showing a potential six-foot bite mark
on the flukes of a humpback whale.

IS MEGALODON STILL ALIVE?

Among the most common marine cryptid or "sea monster" sightings are those of preternaturally large sharks. Anecdotal reports vary greatly when it comes to size. Most describe sharks of thirty or more in length, with one outlandish example claiming a beast that stretched three hundred feet (I kid you not).

Most of these have turned out to be encounters with planktivorous titans such as the whale shark (*Rhincodon typus*). Whale sharks grow to at least forty feet in length, with the largest confirmed individual (McClain et al from their 2015 study, *Sizing Ocean Giants*) reaching sixty-two feet in length. Scaled up from a typical thirty-two-foot, ten-ton specimen, such a giant would weigh somewhere in the realm of seventy tons.

Whale sharks have a disctinctive head shape and color pattern, however, which should, at least in some instances, preclude them from being misinterpreted as a macropredatory shark. Another large plankton feeder, however, the basking (*Cetorhinus maximus*), is similar in both basic body type and coloration to its fellow lamniform, the great white. Basking sharks have reached a documented forty-point-three feet in length, with an estimated weight of eighteen tons. Seen passing beneath one's boat, such a behemoth could easily be interpreted as a 'man-eating monster".

But are all "mega shark" sightings cases of mistaken identity? Based on the evidence I've collected – evidence that we will be examining in detail – the answer is no.

Whale and basking sharks do not have the flesh-cutting teeth of a predator like the great white. And much of our evidence consists of huge bite marks, some of which are quite fresh. This suggests that something is out there, something big and fierce that shears enormous hunks of flesh from its victims. In some cases, the fish responsible may be capable of swallowing a grown man in one bite.

But what is it?

With the exctinct mackerel shark *Carcharocles megalodon* the villain of numerous television shows and movies, people are quick to assume that any report of any oversized shark indicates Megalodon is still with us.

Is it? Is the fifty-foot, fifty-ton whale killer that, according to paleontologists, died out around 3.5 million years ago, still around, eking out a living in the briny depths? If so, why aren't we seeing it? Where does it live? Is there enough food for it? And why don't we see evidence of its feeding?

Before we can answer those and other questions, let's explore a well-known theory of mine that focuses on the largest of the mega-toothed shark's feeding habits and biting technique, and see how it relates to our evidence.

WAS MEGALODON THE WORLD'S LARGEST SCAVENGER?

Otodus megalodon (AKA *Carcharocles megalodon*, AKA *Carcharodon megalodon*) was history's largest known carnivorous fish – an enormous mackerel shark that lived from the early Miocene to the end of the Pliocene Period (approx. 23 million to 3.6 million years ago).

According to my calculations, and based on scaled-up comparisons to estimated lengths of its close relatives, Megalodon reached a maximum length of approximately 56 feet (somewhat akin to Gottfried's 1996 size estimation formula). However, recent studies by the experts have established its maximum at almost fifty 50 feet (Shimada 2019) with an average adult size of around thirty-five. Regardless, a mammoth predator.

Megalodon has been widely touted as a killing machine and, as a result, has been what I call the "primeval protagonist" in numerous novels, starting with Robin Brown's book of the same name, circa 1981. Brown depicted the colossal fish as surviving in the ocean abysses and, when hungry, rising from the depths with zeal to inflict death and destruction upon us unsuspecting surface dwellers.

Since then, the shark has appeared in a plethora of direct-to-video and TV films, including "Shark Attack 3 – Megalodon" where, at eighty feet, it was the size of a large rorqual, and such outrageous turkeys as "Mega-Shark vs Giant Octopus", where it was the size of an ocean liner and could leap ten thousand feet in the air, to snatch passing jets out of the sky.

Spiraling back down to earth: let me say that Megalodon was, without a doubt, an awe-inspiring flesh eater. But cinematic artistry aside, was it the apex predator the public has been led to believe? The answer is yes . . . and no. In works of fiction, the fish's size is often heavily exaggerated. Even I am guilty of it. In my *Kronos Rising: Kraken* novels I featured a *Carcharodon megalodon* by the name of "Ursula" that was up-scaled to eighty-four feet and two hundred tons, in order for it to be capable of battling a similar-sized pliosaur.

Despite this bit of artistic license, I try to incorporate as much actual science into my books as possible. And, as I disclosed in the series, the fossil evidence suggests that, although history's largest carnivorous shark was an efficient and active hunter as a juvenile and sub-adult, as it matured it did less and less hunting until, eventually, it switched over to a diet that was primarily carrion.

This may come as a surprise to some, and there will undoubtedly be a lot of die-hard Megalodon fans who, like *Spinosaurus*'s fans, when their *Tyrannosaurus*-killing "Jurassic Park 3" monster was downgraded to a quadrupedal piscivore, will be offended or even outraged. But the evidence is there, and in abundance. What is this evidence and what brought me to such a conclusion? It's found where one might expect: in the fossils, and combined with physics and good old-fashioned common sense.

Let's start by looking at one of Megalodon's modern-day relatives and the fish it is so often compared to, *Carcharodon carcharias*, AKA the great white shark. Great whites are active predators with sharp and serrated teeth, designed to help them catch, kill, and consume their prey. It is a widely-known fact that the white shark is an active hunter that starts off life preying on fish (including smaller sharks). As it becomes larger and more cumbersome it switches to a diet of marine mammals such as sea lions and elephant seals.[*] It also changes hunting strategies and becomes more of a mugger, creeping along the bottom before rushing up to ambush its more agile prey. Like most hunters, it misses most of the time but, obviously, succeeds often enough to survive. And, like most predators, it supplements its diet with blubber-rich whale carcasses whenever possible.

---

* https://ucmp.berkeley.edu/vertebrates/Doug/shark.html

A great white shark missing a strike on a seal.

The reason the white shark loses agility as it grows and is forced to make this conversion is the chink in its rough-skinned armor – a skeleton made of cartilage. Cartilage is like tire rubber; it's tough and flexible and great when you're six or ten feet long (seven-hundred-pound mako sharks can reach incredible speeds, clear the water in twenty-foot leaps, and maneuver like a jet fighter with thrusters at full burn) but as the animal gets larger, that rubbery skeleton becomes a problem.

Think of a skyscraper; the "skeleton" is made of steel girders, not rubber. If it *was* made of rubber, it would collapse under its own weight. When a shark like a great white reaches fifteen or more feet in length its skeleton can no longer support it as well, even in the water. It starts to lose top-end speed, agility, and the ability to make tight turns. Hence, it changes into an ambush predator.

A perfect example of this are videos of the well-known white shark known as "Deep Blue". Accompanied by environmentalist and "shark whisperer" Ocean Ramsey (and a pair of dolphins), the bulky (and possibly pregnant) shark appears to only be interested in a nearby whale carcass. At a full twenty feet, she seems unwilling or unable to chase the dolphins that frolic all around her, and even ignores one when it rudely nips her or flaps its flukes right in her face.

One would think an apex predator like that would leap at the chance to sink its teeth into fresh, warm dolphin, but she doesn't. Is it because the carcass is there, the proverbial "bird in the hand"? Or is it because both the shark and dolphins know she is so cumbersome that, even at point blank range, they can dance away from her with no problem?

If you have any doubts about the limitations a cartilaginous skeleton imposes on large sharks, all you have to do is compare it to its rival *Orcinus orca*, the killer whale. The world's largest dolphins, Orcas are designed to drag down and kill baleen whales many times their size and have a well-earned reputation for feeding on great whites as well. Pound-for-pound, a killer whale is far more powerful than a white shark. True, it reaches a larger maximum size, yet despite this additional mass it remains faster and more maneuverable. This is due to steely muscles attached and anchored to dense bones. We've all seen videos of an Orca beaching itself to take a seal and then squirming its way back into the water.

Could a five-thousand-pound great white do that? No. In fact, even sleek and agile six-foot white sharks, when stranded, are at the mercy of human beings to drag them back into the surf before they suffocate.

I shot these photos of captive killer whales at SeaWorld, Orlando, when they invited me down for a behind-the-scenes-tour (an attempt to win me over and get me to stop all the bad press I was giving them). In the first shot, the cetaceans are "tail-walking", holding themselves vertically up out of the water using thrusts from their flukes to keep their multi-ton bodies upright. Can sharks do this?

No.

In the second photo, an Orca with more mass than any known white shark is able to hoist both its tail and head up off the deck and, while holding that pose, wriggle itself around so that it spins in full circles – an astonishing display of strength. What would happen to a shark of any species that size if it was pulled up out of the water? It would flap its head and tail in mute protest and then lay there, exhausted, until it had breathed its last.

Captive Orcas displaying astonishing strength, in and out of the water.
Photos by the author.

That may sound harsh, but it's not intended to emasculate sharks – they are superb predators – but rather to help show why Megalodon converted from an active hunter to a consumer of carrion. As it got bigger and heavier and gravity and water resistance exerted more and more influence, the shark invariably became slower and clumsier. Let's revisit *Cetorhinus maximus*, AKA the basking shark. As I mentioned earlier, basking sharks grow quite large, up to forty feet and, like their extant relative, the great white, and their extinct cousin, Megalodon, they are mackerel sharks. Despite the fact that they sometimes fall prey to Orcas, (being otherwise defenseless, one would expect them to have speed on their side) they are surprisingly slow, and lumber along with a typical maximum swim speed of around four mph.*

An exception to the basking shark's speed capabilities was documented in 2018 by Jonathan Houghton from Queen's University in Belfast. While observing the atypical breaching behavior of twenty different basking sharks, he and his colleagues placed a monitoring device on a specimen that measured twenty-six feet in length and weighed around three tons (six thousand pounds).

The shark was able to breach the water at a speed calculated at just over eleven mph, with its huge body clearing the water by around four feet. Houghton estimates that, based on body size, the shark used a similar amount of energy breaching as its warm-blooded cousin the great white does, and was able to travel at a similar speed.**

What is interesting about this is that, in addition to a planktivorous shark like that exhibiting surprising speed, it helps confirm the established principal that the bigger a shark gets, the

---

* http://www.sharkinformation.org/basking-shark/

** https://www.newscientist.com/article/2179238-peaceful-basking-sharks-can-leap-just-as-powerfully-as-great-whites/

slower it gets. Despite ambitious claims of great whites breaching at forty miles per hour, studies of an eleven-point-five-foot individual, which cleared the water by eight feet, showed that it was only able to accelerate to a maximum speed of approximately twenty-one mph.[*]

The difference is mass, drag, and how much stress a cartilaginous skeleton is capable of withstanding when subjected to extreme pressures – in this case, intense muscular contractions. Although a twenty-six-foot, three-ton great white has not yet been documented, let alone filmed breaching, we can safely assume that it would do so at a very slow speed, if at all. Additionally, a maximum speed of twelve mph for a twenty-six-foot fish (a speed that would be reduced even further as its size went up) would be too slow to catch most cetaceans, which are far faster. The gigantean blue whale, for example, has been clocked at nearly thirty mph.[**]

The basking shark and great white; two mackerel sharks that share the same basic body design.

Granted, basking sharks are filter feeders and smaller great whites are far faster (maximum speed estimates are

[*] https://www.theatlantic.com/technology/archive/2011/12/the-physics-of-great-white-sharks-leaping-out-of-the-water-to-catch-seals/249799/

[**] http://www.elasmo-research.org/education/topics/r_haulin%27_bass.htm

typically twenty-five mph* versus the far larger Orca at thirty-five mph), but the principal holds true. When you review footage of "Deep Blue" you can see that, gravid or no, the fish is both slow and lethargic. It doesn't have to move as fast because it has few predators but, more importantly, it can't. It's a matter of anatomy, and it's the same reason why National Geographic, in their recent special, "Sea Monsters: The Definitive Guide" explained why whale sharks don't grow as large as a blue whale. It's the limitations of a cartilaginous skeleton.

My research indicates that Megalodon went through a transitional period as it grew. As a pup, commonly estimated at 7-10 feet at birth, it was a fast and agile hunter, much like a great white of similar size. It fed on fish, whale calves, sea turtles, and sirenids (sea cows). As it grew larger, reaching fifteen to twenty feet in length, it was still an active predator and would have hunted small cetaceans without a doubt. But as it got bigger and clumsier (approx. thirty+ feet) its own mass became its enemy and, at a certain point, it became easier for it to look for alternative sources of food, i.e. carrion.

This is supported by the morphology of the fish's teeth. If we compare the tooth of a young Megalodon (perhaps ten feet in length) to that of a great white, we see a striking similarity in their respective dentition. The teeth are both sharp and highly serrated – designed to impale and rend flesh and inflict horrific wounds. A twenty or even thirty-foot Megalodon would have been a voracious predator, and a deadly one, to be sure.

---

* https://en.wikipedia.org/wiki/Great_white_shark

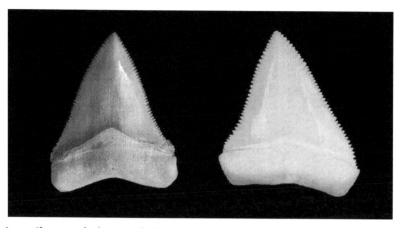

A juvenile Megalodon tooth (image credit M. Stone) and a sub-adult white shark tooth from the author's collection.

But, as that same Megalodon matured into an adult, the serrations on its teeth gradually decreased in size until, eventually, they were barely visible. This is, again, opposed to the great white, whose serrations remain relatively unchanged in number and grow with the shark. As it grew, Megalodon's tooth crowns and roots also changed, converting from serrated blades to blunter, wedge-shaped devices with wide roots and lined with tiny serrations. In terms of tools, they were like chisels with hacksaw-like edges. They were no longer designed primarily for slicing flesh. In fact, that became their secondary purpose. Their primary purpose was to shear through bones.

Some have speculated that this was a hunting strategy, and that Megalodon used its chisel-like teeth to crush the spines of whales. That would be a tall order, as some prehistoric whales were as large as the whales of today. Moreover, attacking a heavily-reinforced bony region is a difficult and dangerous way to make a living. It implies a need to get a firm grip on something that is actively struggling and fighting back. A bleeding fluke or abdominal wound would be a much safer and more efficient strike. The great white's triangular teeth work well for crippling the tails of similar-sized elephant seals, and whale flukes are also vulnerable to those types of bites. So why have thick, chisel-like teeth?

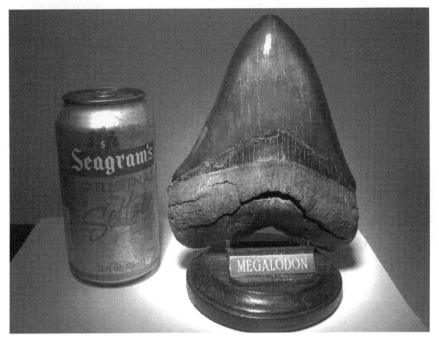

An adult C. megalodon tooth measuring 6.5″ in slant height. Note the tiny serrations and overall mass. (from the author's private collection)

The answer is a need to get at a vast mound of rotting meat. As whales became larger and smarter, and developed defenses like echolocation and a protective herd dynamic, they became harder for adult Megalodons to kill. At forty feet or more, a whale is far more agile than a shark of similar size, and faster, too. Hence, the larger Megalodons found it far easier to switch from active hunting to scavenging, and their teeth adapted to this role as well.

One can imagine a fifty-foot female shark, queen of all she surveys, tracking the scent of a rotting whale carcass – a vast, calorie-rich bounty upon which to satiate herself. The carcass would be days or weeks old, and may well have been the work of the more svelte and agile smaller versions of herself. As she approaches, other scavengers (including smaller Megalodons) scatter. But most of the whale's blubber and outer musculature is already gone – stripped away and consumed.

So, what's left? The nutritious internal organs: the heart, lungs, liver: all waiting to be devoured. The smaller sharks couldn't get to them because of the giant, bony ribs that shielded them, but the huge adult Megalodon, with her gaping nutcracker jaws, could systematically crunch through the dead whale's rib cage, revealing the putrescent bounty within.

Extant sharks make short work of a drifting whale carcass. During the Miocene, hungry-but-ponderous adult Megalodons often found such carcasses stripped by the time they got there.

This is why the teeth of the largest Megalodon sharks became stouter and blunter over time. The fish evolved to clean up whale carcasses that littered the oceans of the world, like sprinkles swirling on a giant cupcake. With no humans to slaughter them and millions of whales swimming around at any given time (before industrial whaling, there were 400,000 blue whales and 1.5 million humpback whales* *alone*), over the course of each year there would have been tens of thousands of whale carcasses to devour. And you can rest assured that the giant sharks did the job. In my novel *Kronos Rising: Kraken*, an *elasmobranchologist* by the name of Judas Cambridge seethes at the memory of his former employer rejecting the Megalodon as a candidate for their bio-weapons program, calling them the "garbage trucks of the seas". A gross exaggeration – the sharks would still kill anything they could catch – but from a "cleanup crew" perspective, he had a point.

*Note: some have balked at the notion that there were tens of thousands of whale carcasses each year. Let's look at that from a numbers perspective and see. Odds are prehistoric whale numbers were at least as high as they were during modern times, so let's use the extant humpback as an example. Humpback whales live an average of 45-50 years. So, let's go with fifty, a nice round number. In theory then, if they were all the same age, in fifty years we would have 1.5 million dead humpbacks (the entire population). Obviously, that's inaccurate. But we can assume, however, that every year around 1/50*th* of their population would expire. That means every year there would be thirty thousand humpback carcasses alone. That's not including all the other species.*

Additionally, what short-sighted detractors fail to realize is that carcasses for adult Megalodons were being provided for them in huge numbers. By whom? Why, by the younger, faster versions of themselves, of course. We have no idea how many Megalodon sharks there were during their heyday, whether it was five thousand or ten times that number (estimates are there are currently over ten thousand great whites). But what we can be sure of is that, for every mature adult in the forty-foot range (fifty footers were incredibly rare, like twenty-foot great whites are today)

* *https://www.theguardian.com/uk/2003/jul/25/science.research*

there were scores, perhaps hundreds of smaller ones in the fifteen to thirty-foot range. And it was those fish that were killing prehistoric baleen whales like the similar-sized Cetotherium. And what were they leaving behind after feeding on said whales?

Carcasses. Many, many carcasses.

If all that isn't enough, let's look at things from an evolutionary perspective. The chart below demonstrates what many paleontologists believe to be the lineage of *C. megalodon* (fossil teeth from my personal collection). As you can see, the adult sharks' teeth changed over time as the animals grew and their diets changed. Whereas the earliest "mega-tooth" sharks like *C. auriculatus* were primarily fish eaters and most likely remained active predators from birth to death (note: maximum length for *Auriculatus* is around thirty feet), later specimens like *C. chubutensis* and Megalodon fed mainly on thick-boned marine mammals and gradually evolved those familiar bone-gnashing chompers.

Actually, let's take a brief look at Chubutensis and do a quick comparison with Megalodon. *C. chubutensis* was a large mackerel shark with teeth up to five inches long and a body size of up to forty feet. (*Note: C. chubutensis and C. megalodon had an overlap of some 2.4 million years where the two fish existed at the same time. It is believed that a population of Chubutensis split off, evolving into Megalodon, while the remainder of the species remained unchanged until their eventual extinction*). Chubutensis was large and powerful, a formidable hunter, but as it passed the 30-foot mark, it is likely that it, too, experienced the same skeletal-based limitations its larger cousin did. It is plausible then that, as a twenty-five-ton adult, Chubutensis often shared carcasses with Megalodon, as tiger sharks and great whites sometimes do today.

Note: at no point am I saying that either C. chubutensis or C. megalodon were not carnivores. They were flesh-eaters of the highest order and woe to any wounded cetacean or foundering sea turtle they encountered. But when it came to tackling big, agile prey, the very anatomy of these behemoths hamstrung them and forced them to behave more like giant hyenas – making kills if they could, but primarily chowing down on the abundant rotting carcasses their amazing olfactory systems led them to (an unfair comparison, I suppose; the much-maligned hyena is actually an active predator, but you get the point).

Last but not least, if my theory still needs any "reinforcing", let me point out the damage that is often present on the most prized fossil Megalodon teeth. Below, is a closeup of a tooth from my private collection. It measures 6.5" in slant height, over five inches in width, and weighs twenty ounces – a decent specimen. It is what is commonly described as a maxillary (upper jaw) anterior primary tooth or "impact tooth", meaning it is among the first to strike prey. The tip of the tooth exhibits what paleontologists refer to as "feeding damage". Before it was lost, the shark's tooth tip was crushed as it fed.

This type of damage typically effects the largest and most commercially desirable teeth, and takes away from the value of found specimens. But why do broken or mashed down tips primarily plague the largest of teeth (usually over five inches) and not the smaller ones?

This type of breakage is not the result of a sudden impact, i.e. smashing into the body of a whale, jaws agape, in order to crush its spine. If that were the case, and with tooth enamel being harder and stronger than whale ribs, the tooth would not incur damage like that. Rather, the weak link would be the tooth's insertion point at the gum line where it is anchored into comparatively soft cartilage. Instead of breaking, the tooth would have been shorn away, as sometimes happens when white sharks strike a surf board or kayak.

The tip damage we see in large Megalodon teeth is caused by what any engineer will tell you is compression damage. The shark is biting into (oft times repeatedly) a hard substance, i.e. rib bone, and the repeated stress, all focused on the point of that chisel-shaped tooth, causes the tooth tip to collapse. This happens when steady pressure is applied, and typically against a stationary target. This explains why it is mainly the biggest teeth that suffer this type of damage. The animal is too large to successfully hunt the more agile whales it preys upon and is forced to fall back on scavenging to survive: biting through bone repeatedly to get the portions of the whale that smaller predators and scavengers missed.

This combined evidence leaves little to the imagination. A white shark (or a sub-adult Megalodon) is/would-have-been an active hunter with serrated, dagger-like teeth evolved to inflict massive wounds that caused hemorrhaging and death. Those are the jaws of a predator. Whereas the chisel-shaped, hacksaw-edged teeth of an adult Megalodon (shown beside them) are more like a nutcracker – breaking open a hard shell to get at the juicy prizes others have left behind. That is the hallmark of a scavenger, and a hellaciously large one at that.

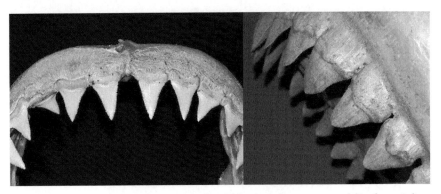

White shark teeth left (image credit: Robert Robertson - public domain),
Megalodon teeth right.

One additional point: My theory that adult Megalodons were most likely primary scavengers may also shed light on what caused their decline. Toxic algae blooms, loss of plankton, and other harsh and sudden changes in the ecology of the seas that wiped out populations of small baleen whales would have had a tremendous impact on this giant hunter/scavenger. The smaller (~thirty-foot) whales were paramount. Giant baleen whales living in pods were too big and powerful for the predatory, sub-adult Megalodons to prey upon, and too fast and organized for the adults to take down. The loss or even a sharp reduction in the number of smaller whales could have had a domino effect that decimated the shark's numbers. A reduction in whale populations by 80%-90% would have, naturally, reduced the number of available carcasses by the same amount.

No carcasses meant no food. No food meant no brood stock. And no brood stock meant no future generations.

In summary, it is likely that *C. megalodon*, the fifty-foot, forty-ton super-shark, was an active predator as a pup and adolescent and, as it approached sexual maturity (approx. 30+ feet) it began to change. Its teeth grew steadily stouter and more finely serrated and it gradually converted from a hunter into a scavenger until, as a 40+foot adult, the majority of its food came from drifting cetacean remains (and an occasional pregnant or wounded whale).

We can also conclude that it is very likely that reduced whale populations and the subsequent lack of whale carcasses had a substantial impact on the shark's survival, as it would have directly affected the number of breeding adults and drastically reduced its numbers. This was, in all likelihood, a contributing factor to Megalodon's demise; it simply got so huge that the inherent limits of its cartilaginous skeleton forced it into a more vulture-like role. And, with no carrion to feed on, the colossal shark eventually disappeared.

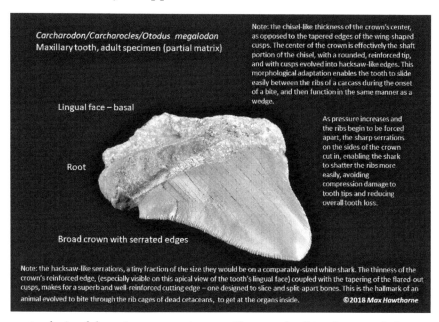

Note: the chisel-like thickness of the crown's center, as opposed to the tapered edges of the wing-shaped cusps. The center of the crown is effectively the shaft portion of the chisel, with a rounded, reinforced tip, and with cusps evolved into hacksaw-like edges. This morphological adaptation enables the tooth to slide easily between the ribs of a carcass during the onset of a bite, and then function in the same manner as a wedge.

As pressure increases and the ribs begin to be forced apart, the sharp serrations on the sides of the crown cut in, enabling the shark to shatter the ribs more easily, avoiding compression damage to tooth tips and reducing overall tooth loss.

Carcharodon/Carcharocles/Otodus megalodon
Maxillary tooth, adult specimen (partial matrix)

Lingual face – basal

Root

Broad crown with serrated edges

Note: the hacksaw-like serrations, a tiny fraction of the size they would be on a comparably-sized white shark. The thinness of the crown's reinforced edge, (especially visible on this apical view of the tooth's lingual face) coupled with the tapering of the flared-out cusps, makes for a superb and well-reinforced cutting edge – one designed to slice and split apart bones. This is the hallmark of an animal evolved to bite through the rib cages of dead cetaceans, to get at the organs inside. ©2018 *Max Hawthorne*

Analysis of the primary anterior maxillary teeth of *Otodus megalodon*.
By the author.

TRUNKO BUNKO

I'm a firm believer that there are large, undocumented sea creatures inhabiting all of the world's oceans. It's practically a mathematical certainty. Whether they're thought-to-be-extinct examples of known species that have, for whatever reason, disappeared from the fossil record and then reappeared (Lazarus taxon), or they're entirely new ones, remains to be seen. One supposed "sea monster", however, I am firmly convinced is just the result of misidentification. That would be "Trunko", a large animal that was seen battling Orcas off the coast of South Africa in 1924, and whose body washed ashore ten days later.

I don't think Trunko was a sea monster. I think it was a male whale of some kind – probably a right or gray whale – and possibly a white one. It's a known fact that whale carcasses often turn white as they rot and the skin comes off. Moreover, the collagen in decaying whale blubber tends to break down into fibers – long strands that are often erroneously interpreted as being hair.

Of course, those facts are largely irrelevant in this case. Eye witnesses, who described Trunko as being white "like a polar bear", watched as the creature fought back against an aggressive pair of killer whales. Albino and partly-white right and gray whales, although rare, do happen. Moreover, a white whale would make for an inviting target for opportunistic Orcas, as it would stand out, and be easier to track, once it attempted to flee.

An albino right whale. Could one of these have been Trunko?

In terms of the creature's supposed "trunk", I believe this was simply the bull whale's sexual organ. The organs of male whales can be huge – blue whales hold the record at around ten feet.*

My theory on the identity of Trunko's "trunk" is supported by the examination of the carcass, which stated that the tapering trunk was attached directly to the torso of the animal. (for details, see the accompanying screenshots of the complete Trunko Wikipedia article before much of it was redacted). Gray whales can reach a length of 49 feet, with a fluke span of 10-12 feet, and a penile length of around six feet. Interestingly, Trunko's rotting remains were measured at 47 feet in length with a 10-foot-wide "tail" and a tapered "trunk" that was five feet in length. That fits gray whale dimensions nicely.

Furthermore, I disagree with supposed claims that the "monster" was a globster (a large, gelatinous mass of rotting whale

---

* https://roaring.earth/the-longest-penis-in-the-animal-kingdom/

blubber that has separated from the carcass). Firstly, Orcas aren't likely to play with a foul-smelling, twenty-to-thirty-ton glob of putrescence for three hours straight (the length of the documented battle). If they had such tendencies, we'd see them appropriating drifting whale remains from great whites. But we don't. However, Orca attacks on large whales are proven to take several hours.[*]

In addition, the fight was witnessed and, over the course of the battle, "Trunko" repeatedly used its "lobster-like" tail (i.e. flukes) to fend off the killer whales. Lengthy battles between Orcas and larger cetaceans often drag on as they wear down and exhaust their quarry. Moreover, baleen whales and even sperm whales commonly use their tails as a defense against killer whales. These combined facts strongly suggest that Trunko was a living creature, not a drifting mass of rotting blubber.

Assertions that the creature's "trunk" was simply a rib or some other loose piece of bone are, in my opinion, a bit of a stretch (pun intended). Loose ribs don't stay attached to slabs of decaying fat, especially when slammed repeatedly and tossed twenty feet in the air by killer whales (again, for *3 hours*). Witnesses saw the trunk and even measured it. I am sure they would know a curved, protruding piece of bone if they saw one. Instead, it was described as "elephantine". This was undoubtedly what remained of the unfortunate whale's penis.

Male whales often expose their organs when around females, sometimes even in groups, and their huge genitalia have reportedly been mistaken for everything from sea serpents to giant squid battling whales. If that's not enough, if you look at this head-on picture that was taken of Trunko's carcass, it bears a remarkable similarity to that of a baleen whale, especially when viewed head-on.

---

[*] https://en.wikipedia.org/wiki/Killer_whale#Mammals_and_birds

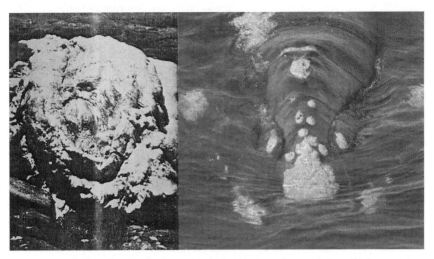

A photo of "Trunko" on the left compared to a right whale.
(image credit: Margate Museum)

I don't believe there is any doubt. Based on witness description, behavior, measurements, description of the body shape, tail
width, and an elephantine "trunk" protruding from the carcass,
Trunko was not a globster. It was simply a baleen whale that
fought and lost a battle against a tenacious pair of killer whales
and washed ashore later as a shark-ravaged, decomposing mass.
It *is* possible that the beached carcass was not the same animal
that was seen being attacked by Orcas. It is believed that, before
the rise of commercial whaling, gray whales were the killer
whales' primary target species. So, in 1924, attacks like that
would have been fairly common. However, once again, the witness descriptions and associated measurements of the remains
still suggest that it was, indeed, an actual, decaying carcass and
not a globster.

I love my sea monsters; but in the end, whether carcass or
globster, this ain't one of them.

For the full, unredacted Wikipedia page on Trunko see screen-shots below or go to:

https://ipfs.io/ipfs/QmXoypizjW3WknFiJnKLwHCnL72
vedxjQkDDP1mXWo6uco/wiki/Trunko.html#cite_note-10

Trunko

Trunko is the nickname for an animal or globster[1] reportedly sighted in Margate, South Africa, on 25 October 1924, according to an article entitled "Fish Like A Polar Bear" published in the 27 December 1924, edition of London's *Daily Mail*. The animal was reputedly first seen off the coast battling two killer whales, which fought the unusual creature for three hours. It used its tail to attack the whales and reportedly lifted itself out of the water by about 20 feet. One of the witnesses, Hugh Ballance, described the animal as looking like a "giant polar bear" during a final fight.

Trunko	
Artistic depiction of Trunko being mauled by orcas by Bill Asmussen	
Other name(s)	The Margate Monster
Country	South Africa
Region	Africa
Habitat	Water

Description

The creature reputedly washed up on Margate Beach but despite being there for 10 days, no scientist ever investigated the carcass while it was beached, so no reliable description has been published, and until September 2010 it was assumed that no photographs of it had ever been published. Some people who have never been identified were reported to have described the animal as possessing snowy-white fur, an elephantine trunk, a lobster-like tail, and a carcass devoid of blood.

While it was beached, the animal was measured by beach-goers and turned out to be 47 ft (14 m) in length, 10 ft (3 m) wide, and 5 ft (1.5 m) high, with the trunk's length being 5 ft (1.5 m), the trunk's diameter 14 in (36 cm), the tail 10 ft (3 m), and the fur being 8 in (20 cm) long. The trunk was said to be attached directly to the animal's torso, as no head was visible on the carcass. For this feature, the animal was dubbed "Trunko" by British cryptozoologist Karl Shuker in his 1996 book *The Unexplained*.[2] In the 27 March 1925, edition of the *Charleroi Mail*, in Charleroi, Pennsylvania, an article entitled "Whales Slain By Hairy Monster" reported that whales there were killed by a strange creature which was washed up on a beach exhausted and fell unconscious, but made its way back into the ocean and swam away after 10 days, never to be seen again.

In March 2011, a fourth photograph of Trunko was discovered in the archives of Margate Museum in South Africa by Bianca Baldi.[7]

On March 29, 2016 paleo-author Max Hawthorne released his own findings on Trunko, with an article featured on the cryptozoological site Cryptomundo entitled "Sea Monster 'Exposed'". In his article, Hawthorne stated that Trunko was not a globster per se, but rather, the rotting remains of a male baleen whale that had been attacked and killed by Orcas. He also stated that the creature's "trunk" was simply the cetacean's exposed sexual organ.[8]

Hawthorne's findings were hotly contested on social media by Karl Shuker, who defended his position by saying that the "trunk" was most likely one of the dead whale's ribs, still attached to the globster. On April 27, 2016, Hawthorne released more detailed findings on his personal blog:.[9] In his article "Trunko Bunko", he concluded that "Trunko" was most likely a white or whitish bull right whale, a rare but not unknown commodity, and that the whale's bright coloration made it an inviting target for opportunistic killer whales. The description of the battle by witnesses, including the creature using its "lobster-like" tail to defend itself from the Orcas, the description and measurements of the carcass, including fluke proportions which would match a whale of that species, and the "trunk" being attached to the middle of the body, appeared to bear out his claims. Lastly, Hawthorne compared one of the recently found photos of Trunko and showed that, structurally, its skull region bore an uncanny resemblance to that of a right whale when viewed head-on, even in an advanced state of decay.

On July 2016 the debate of globster-versus-carcass was revisited when one of Shuker's colleagues, cryptozoologist Scott Mardis, interviewed Hawthorne on an episode of Monster-X Radio. When the topic of Trunko arose, Mardis conceded that the photographic evidence suggested the head portion of Trunko bore a marked similarity to that of a right whale. He went on to state that he and his colleagues had altered their position and accepted the possibility that, perhaps, the whale's skull and other bones were still contained in the globster. Hawthorne responded to this by stating that, by the very definition of a globster, Trunko no longer qualified as such, and his own theory was therefore proven.[10]

See also

- Cryptozoology

NOTE: Per a conversation I had with Dr. Karl Shuker (the cryptozoologist who coined the name "Trunko") on 3/12/2020, he does not, and has never believed that Trunko was a whale carcass and asserts that it was, in his opinion, a globster. Any assertion that he had changed his opinion, as previously stated by cryptozoologist Scott Mardis on Monster-X Radio, is erroneous. Dr. Shuker stands by his original opinion that the remains found were a globster. I respect his research and I appreciate him taking the time to clarify his position.

GHOST FISH?

Of all the incidents I've investigated for this book, this one was the toughest to write about. It's outside my area of expertise, and also outside my comfort zone. But it is something that I experienced and, for anyone interested in the paranormal, I suppose it's worth sharing.

The incident in question took place a decade or so ago. I don't recall the year. I was temporarily out-of-state at the time, and there were several local ponds near me that my dad and I used to fish. They weren't big or glamorous, but the fishing was usually good. And, since I used to spend an inordinate amount of time trying to put my late father on fish (he said it was included in his retirement package), high-yield spots that were only a few minutes' drive were eminently desirable.

Starting earlier that spring, my dad and I had been trying our luck night-fishing a local river. Our target species was catfish. Sure, the local ponds occasionally produced channel cats in the ten-to-twelve-pound class, but if we wanted to catch a monster, we figured a big body of water was our best bet.

We found out via word of mouth that the bait that worked best for channels was fresh pieces of carp fillet, with the skin still on. The old-timers were right. The meat was pungent, incredibly oily, and tough as hell – impossible for small predators to just pull off the hook. We'd put out a few rods baited with two-inch hunks of carp, toss a handful of chunks out as chum, then sit back and wait.

We rarely got skunked.

The only downside of this kind of fishing was the preparatory work I had to do before my dad would drive out for one of his weekend visits. I had to acquire bait. Fresh bait. And that meant doing something I don't enjoy. I had to catch and kill a carp.

That might sound unmanly to some, especially coming from a "Master Angler" like myself. But I'm typically a catch-and-release angler. If I'm going to keep fish for the table (flounder for example) they're tossed into a bucket or livewell to expire and it's out of my hands. I've actually given up several all-tackle world records (blue shark and nurse shark, to be precise) simply because I refused to kill the fish.

So, yes, I'm softhearted. Whatever.

When it came to procuring carp for bait, there was one pond I liked to target. The fish were plentiful and not overly large – typically 8-10 pounds – which was a good size. The fillets could be cut up and frozen, and would last several trips. To humanely dispatch the fish, I carried a hard rubber mallet. I'd give it a good whack on the head and put it out of its misery. Then it was tossed into a heavy-gauge contractor bag, placed on ice in the cooler, and taken home to make the necessary preparations.

Unfortunately, that particular day was unseasonably hot and humid and I had missed the early morning bite. The fish had shut down from the heat and, after a few hours, I decided to pull up stakes and try another body of water.

The pond closest to home was small – a few acres at most. It had carp, but I knew from experience that they were often bigger than what I had in mind. I hated the idea of killing a big "gamefish" that my dad would enjoy fighting and landing (in Europe, German carp are as popular as largemouth bass are here, tournaments and all).

I parked in a small parking area adjacent to the pond, grabbed my gear and folding chair, made my way down the hill, and quickly set up shop. I tossed out some corn to attract the fish, put a few rods out, and started doing the inevitable. Waiting.

In retrospect, I'd seen a bunch of bouquets of flowers, notes, and even a few stuffed animals, piled up against a fence near where I'd parked, but I paid them no mind. I'd just gotten back from vacation, had promised my dad to put him on some fish, and I was focused on acquiring bait.

As I said, it was hot. As in Amazonian hot and muggy; the kind of weather that makes you wish you could shed your skin like a snake does. After almost two more hours, I still hadn't had a bite, and I began to worry that my day's fishing would end up producing nothing but a big donut.

Then I got the hit.

It was one of those long, sizzling runs that comes from a big fish. I was using light tackle, and it's likely that, if the pond hadn't been so small, he'd have spooled me. Luckily, after a good 7-8 minutes, the fish tired and I got it into the net.

That was when the trouble started.

The first problem was the fish was sizable – over twenty pounds. That was twice the size I was looking for, and one of the biggest fish I'd ever seen come out of that pond. It would've been a shame to kill it.

Large carp caught and released by the author at a local pond.

Still, I'd promised my dad another productive night catfishing trip on the river wall, and I needed bait. I shook my head, looked at the exhausted fish lying there, and said aloud, "Sorry, fella. I guess this isn't your lucky day."

With that, I pulled out my black contractor bag and fluffed it open. Then I reached for my rubber mallet.

The fish took one look and started crying. I don't mean tears; I mean it was making these low whimpering noises, the kind a frightened child makes. And the entire time it was staring at the mallet I held with actual terror in its eyes.

I know carp are capable of making grunting sounds. I've heard a few do it while fishing the Merrimac River in Massachusetts. But this didn't sound like that. It literally sounded like the fish knew what was about to happen and was crying out in fear. It was so heart-wrenching that, after a moment's hesitation, I couldn't go through with it. I just couldn't. I dropped the mallet, reached for the fish and told it, "I guess it's your lucky day after all."

I quickly set my camera on my folding chair's arm to take a few timed photos, then placed the carp back in the water. I held if there in the shallows, swishing it back and forth to get water flowing over its gills. Once I could tell it had its strength back, I let it go. I felt good watching it as it powered off.

It was then that the weirdest part of my day took place. Forced to accept that Ava's grandfather would have to settle for whatever potluck we'd have at one of the local ponds, I grudgingly packed up my gear and trudged back up the hill toward my truck.

Closeup of the mysterious carp released by the author.

As I finished putting my chair, rods et al in the back and closed the hatch, I noticed all the flowers and stuff I'd mentioned earlier. I walked over and took a look. I realized it was some sort of memorial. The person who'd passed away was, from what I could glean, a teenager from a local high school. A dreadful feeling came over me, and I began to wonder if they'd died in the pond.

I realized then that nobody else had shown up to fish while I was there, which was unusual; there were always a few anglers around. Then I remembered seeing a few weird bright red or pink sticks – markers of some kind, I suppose – that had been embedded in the bottom of the pond and protruded up from the water.

After jotting down the deceased teen's name (I don't recall it now and wouldn't publish it here, regardless), I went home and Googled it. Sure enough, while we'd been away on vacation, they'd disappeared and, after a frantic multi-day search, had been pulled from the water by police divers. Someone told me that some luckless fisherman had spotted the body, but I have no idea if that was true.

The story behind the teen's death was tragic. Their car had been found in the pond's parking lot. A search had been quickly implemented, but nothing came of it.

Until days later, that is.

From what I recall – and it's been many years – the police listed the death as a suicide. Supposedly, substance abuse had played a part. They'd parked the car and ran down the hill into the water and drowned. They also said there was no evidence of assault.

I'm no expert, but some of that seems a bit odd to me. Who decides to drown themselves in a shallow, dirty pond filled with snapping turtles? The muddy water is only a yard deep in most places, maybe 5-6 feet at the far end, but you'd have to wade way far out to get to it.

True, if alcohol or the like was involved, one's judgment might be askew. A sudden urge to go swimming, coupled with an impaired condition, could've resulted in accidental drowning. I believe a suicide note was announced, however, so maybe it was intentional after all.

I don't know. What I do know is I felt like a world-class heel for fishing in the place where someone so young had been pulled out of the water, just a day or two earlier. Granted, I had no way of knowing that, but it didn't change anything.

It's strange, but the one thing that stuck with me about that senseless tragedy was my experience with that carp. It's going to make me sound like I wear a tinfoil sleep cap to bed, but after what happened, I can't help but consider the possibility of spiritual transference. Spirits are real. I've had encounters with ghosts. Real, physical encounters. Some have been amiable, some not.

In fact, for the better part of two decades now, I've been blessed to have a deceased loved one who watches over me – someone who has literally saved my life on multiple occasions. And I'm talking *physically intervened* to save my life, including ripping open the door of a burning SUV that I was trapped inside of. She's a real-life guardian angel. You can laugh at that, and that's fine. It's completely understandable. But, keep in mind, many people would wish they had such a protector.

The point of all this is, I wonder if that teen's death – suicide or no – was such a traumatic thing that perhaps their spirit didn't leave. Maybe it somehow took up temporary residence in the only large life form in the vicinity . . . a carp.

It sounds crazy, I know. But if you were there and heard that fish crying like I did, and saw its eyes, you might wonder the same thing.

All I can say is, thank God I didn't kill it. I hope that adolescent's family and friends managed to come to terms with the loss. And I pray that they, themselves, found peace.

Kraken Sightings

Since man first dared to set sail across fathomless and often fearsome seas, legends have abounded of marine monsters – creatures of horrendous size and strength that cracked ships in two and dragged screaming sailors to their deaths. Chief among these was the Kraken, a beast described by the ancient Vikings as being so huge that it could swallow whales whole and that, when resting on the surface, was often mistaken for an island.

18th century woodcut of a giant octopus attacking a ship.

By modern times, sightings of the Kraken had been dismissed as exaggerated encounters with *Architeuthis dux*, AKA the giant squid. As *Architeuthis* remains began to wash ashore, they were studied in detail. At a maximum estimated weight of around 2,000 lbs., although the deep-dwelling squid was an impressive animal, it fell far short of being the mythical colossus the Kraken was reported to be.

The largest documented squid was found on November 2nd, 1878. It was an Architeuthis that was discovered beached at Thimble Thickle Bay, Newfoundland. The dying squid measured a full twenty from the tip of its caudal fin to its beak. Its longest tentacles measured thirty-five feet, giving it a total length of fifty-five feet.

But is the giant squid really the Kraken of myth and legend? And, if not, is there any evidence that such a creature ever existed? The proof may lie in the fossil record. In the summer of 2011, Dr. Mark McMenamin, a paleontologist and professor of geology at Mount Holyoke College, discovered evidence of what he christened the *Triassic Kraken,* an octopus-like creature estimated at one hundred feet in length. Judging by a collection of huge skeletons that were found with their ribs crushed or necks snapped, McMenamin's mammoth cephalopod liked to prey on *Shonisaurus popularis,* a prehistoric Ichthyosaur the size of an extant humpback whale.

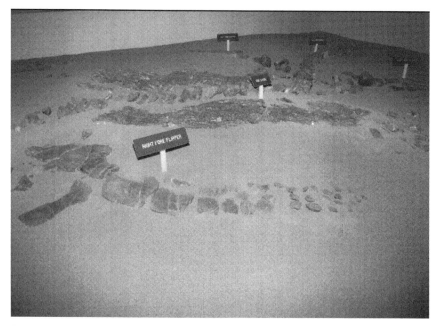

A bus-sized *Shonisaurus* skeleton. The rib cage of this and other specimens show matching breaks on both sides of the rib cage – ligature marks, as if steely bands wrapped around the animal and crushed it. The researchers believe this to be the calling card of the Triassic Kraken. Image credit: Nevada State Museum, Las Vegas, Nevada.

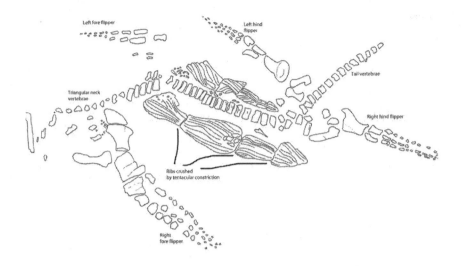

A matching sketch of the *Shonisaurus popularis* skeleton, formerly on display at the Nevada State Museum, Las Vegas, Nevada, and detailing the damage inflicted on it. Artwork by Mark McMenamin, used here by permission of the artist.

One can imagine the scene as this terrifying creature rose from the abyss to stalk the sea's apex predators. Seizing them in its powerful tentacles, it strangled them or crushed them to death, before dragging them back to its midden to feast on their flesh.

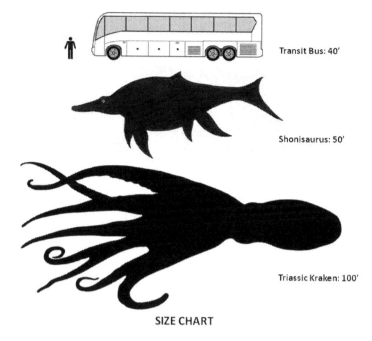

Transit Bus: 40'

Shonisaurus: 50'

Triassic Kraken: 100'

SIZE CHART

Est. size of the theorized Triassic Kraken compared to its prey,
Shonisaurus popularis.

We know that a prehistoric version of the Kraken may have existed. But could this true-to-life deep-sea monster, or one of its descendants, still be alive today, 215 million years later? It may be possible. *Vampyroteuthis infernalis,* the tiny Vampire squid that dwells in the depths of today's oceans, has characteristics of both octopi and squids. This suggests that a transition form is feasible, and an evolution from octopus to squid may have taken place. But, if so, what would a kaiju-sized squid eat?

The answer is whales.

Whales, you say? But don't they eat squid?

Put succinctly, although *Physeter macrocephalus,* AKA the sperm whale, does, indeed, regularly feed on both the giant and colossal squid, it is possible that one of preternatural proportions could kill and feed on even a bull sperm whale. The whale's jaws only possess teeth in the mandible (lower jaw) and are designed to pierce. They're pegs that help them grasp slippery squid. However, they are not capable of biting pieces out of or severing large prey items and, as such, are not designed for combat with a cephalopod as big or bigger than the whale itself.

Moreover, baleen whales have no teeth with which to defend themselves. If attacked by a mammoth squid they would be forced to rely on their size and strength, and possibly blows from their flukes, to save them.

The biggest weakness any cetacean has in a whale-versus-squid battle is their need to surface for air. If embroiled in a deepwater battle with an opponent that has no such weakness for too long, the whale will eventually run out of air. If it cannot spout, it will drown.

Physical evidence

The first proof of the giant squid (beyond whalers finding tentacles in sperm whale stomachs or sucker scars on their skin) consisted of carcasses washed ashore in Newfoundland, starting in 1875[*]. Given that the first photographs of a live specimen weren't taken until 2004[**] and the first live video footage wasn't filmed until 2012[***], our knowledge of *Architeuthis* is still limited (note: that is assuming that sightings of squid far larger than the norm are the same genus). Estimations and extrapolations of maximum size are based on the mantle length of measured specimens, as well as the beaks found in the bellies of sperm whales.

That limits things. The law of averages dictates that the odds of a beached specimen being the maximum size for any

[*] https://en.wikipedia.org/wiki/
List_of_giant_squid_specimens_and_sightings#History_of_discovery
[**] https://www.newscientist.com/article/
dn8064-first-pictures-of-live-giant-squid-in-its-natural-habitat/
[***] https://www.cnn.com/2013/01/09/world/asia/japan-giant-squid/
index.html

given marine species is remarkably slim. For example, we know that, per Soviet whaling records, the largest bull sperm whales once reached 85 feet in length. Yet the biggest specimen that has washed ashore was only 59 feet long.[*]

Whales are airbreathers whose carcasses often float. Hence, they are far more easily washed ashore than a mollusk with no lungs and the same body density as water. Additionally, giant squid are abyssal creatures, typically living thousands of feet down. Only the smaller specimens would swim close to shore to begin with. Therefore, the odds are only smaller individuals end up getting beached (perhaps, due to them fleeing from predators).

Lastly, it would be incredibly irresponsible for any researcher to assume that beaks found in the stomachs of sperm whales is an indicator of maximum size. Barring some unforeseen factor, a cachalot is only going to attempt to feed upon a squid that it is capable of both killing and consuming. Hence, in this situation, sampling bias is a given. A sperm whale would almost certainly ignore a squid as large as it, and would flee from one that was bigger than it was. If it didn't then it, itself, might well be viewed as prey.

Historical sightings

Until additional evidence comes to light, anecdotal reports are the only evidence that currently exists of truly monstrous squid. Over the last 200 years, there have been several documented, eyewitness accounts of specimens that qualify as being of Kraken-like proportions.

Delia incident

June 21, 1818, off the coast of Maine. While sailing between Boston, MA and Hallowell, ME, the crew of the packet *Delia*

---

[*] https://en.wikipedia.org/wiki/List_of_sperm_whale_strandings

witnessed a life-or-death struggle between a "sea serpent" and an adult humpback whale.

Per an entry in Rev. Henry T. Cheever's, *The Whale and His Captors* (1850):

At six o'clock in the afternoon of June 21st, in the packet Delia, plying between Boston and Hallowell, when Cape Ann bore west southwest about two miles, steering north northeast, Captain Shubael West, and fifteen others on board with him, saw an object directly ahead which he had no doubt was the sea serpent, or the creature so often described under that name, engaged in fight with a large hump-back whale that was endeavoring to elude the attack.

The serpent threw up his tail from twenty-five to thirty feet in a perpendicular direction, striking the whale by it with tremendous blows rapidly repeated, which were distinctly heard and very loud for two or three minutes. They then both disappeared, moving in a west-southwest direction, but after a few minutes reappeared in shore of the packet, and about under the sun, the reflection of which was so strong as to prevent their seeing so distinctly as at first, when the serpent's fearful blows with his tail were repeated and clearly heard as before.

They again went down for a short time, and then came up to the surface under the packet's larboard quarter, the whale appearing first and the serpent in pursuit, who was again seen to shoot up his tail as before, which he held out of water some time, waving it in the air before striking, and at the same time, while his tail remained in this position, he raised his head fifteen or twenty feet, as if taking a view of the surface of the sea. After being seen in this position a few minutes, the serpent and whale again sunk and disappeared, and neither were seen after by any on board. It was Captain West's opinion that the whale was trying to escape, as he spouted but once at a time on coming to the surface, and the last time he appeared he went down before the serpent came up.[*]

---

[*] http://whalesite.org/anthology/cheever.htm#chapvii

The "sea serpent" referenced was undoubtedly a gigantic squid of some kind, with the tentacles being interpreted as being said serpent's coils, tail, etc. With humpbacks being planktivorous, and with the whale managing to break free from its opponent only to be reattacked, we can only assume that this incident was one of intended predation. Many such reports involving sperm whales are dismissed with the assumption that the whale was feeding on the squid, and that what the witnesses saw was the prey's death throes. In this case, however, a non-predatory whale was deliberately and tenaciously attacked by what sounds like a huge cephalopod.

Arms rising thirty feet out of the water suggests an unorthodox method of attack – one not normally seen in smaller squid, but easily adapted for a huge one pitted against a massive prey item. It also suggests an *Architeuthis* (sans the two long feeding tentacles) well over eighty feet in length. This would be plenty big enough to wear down and feed upon even a fifty-foot bull humpback.

Engraving from *The Whale and His Captors,*
by Henry T. Cheever, showing the Delia incident.

Delia incident recreation showing possible size comparison between the whale and its attacker.

Pearl incident

1874, Bay of Bengal, India. Three days after departing Galle, the *Pearl*, a 150-foot schooner (there are conflicting reports in terms of whether the schooner was 150 feet or 150 tons – a 150-ton schooner is around 124' long with a 24' beam*) was reported to have been attacked and sunk by an immense squid. The incident was corroborated by witnesses aboard a passing steamer called the *Strathowen*. The skipper's account states:

1 was lately the skipper of the Pearl schooner, 150 ton?, as tight a little craft as ever sailed the seas, with a crew of six men. We were bound from the Mauritius to Rangoon in ballast to return with paddy, and had put in at Galle for water. Three days out we fell becalmed in the bay | lat. 8 deg. 50 sec. N., long. 84 deg. 5 sec. E. Jon May 10 1 about sp. si. (8 bells I know had gone), we sighted a two-masted screw on our port quarter, five about, or six miles off; very soon after, as we lay motionless, a great mass rose slowly out of the sea, about half a mile oil' on our larboard side, and remained spread out as it were and stationary ; it looked like the back of a huge whale, but it was sloped less, and was of a brownish color; even at that distance it seemed much longer than our craft, and seemed to be basking in the sun.

"What be that?" 1 sang out to the mate. "Blest if 1 knows; bearing its size, color and shape, it aught be a whale," replied Tom Scott. "And it ain't the sea serpent," said one of the crew, "for he's too round for I bet ere critter." 1 went into the cabin for my rifle, as I was preparing to fire, Bill Darling, a Newfoundlander, put up his hand, "Have a care master ; that ere is a squid, and he'll capsize us if you hurt him." Sailing at the idea, I let fire and hit him, and with that he shook, there was a great ripple all around him, and he began to move. "Out with all your axes and knives," shouted Bill, "and cut at any part of him that comes aboard; look alive, and Lord help us!" Not aware of the danger, and never having seen or heard of such a monster, I gave no orders, and it was no use touching the helm or ropes to get out of the way. By this time three of the crew, Bill included, had found axes, and one a rusty cutlass, and all were looking over the ship's side at the advancing monster.

We could now see a huge oblong mass moving by jerks just under the surface of the water, and an enormous train following. The oblong body was at least half the size of our vessel in length, and just as thick; the wake or train might have been 100 feet long. In the time that I have taken to write this the brute struck us, and the ship quivered under the thud. In another moment, monstrous arms like trees seized the vessel, and she heeled over; in another second the monster was on board, squeezed in between the two masts, Rill screaming, "Slash for your lives!" but our slashing was of no avail, for the brute, holding on by his arms, slipped bis vast body overboard and pulled the vessel down with him on her beam ends. We were thrown into the water at once and just as I went over, I caught sight of one of the crew, either Bill or Tom Fielding, squashed up between the mast and one of those awful aims. For a few seconds our ship lay on her beam ends, then filled and went *down. Another of the crew must have been sucked down, for you only picked up five. The rest you know. I can't tell who ran up the ensign.*[*]

According to eye witness statements, the squid surfaced before launching its assault, and may have been provoked by being shot at. It was a brownish color and, according to the captain, had an "oblong body" at least half as long as the schooner and just as thick. That sounds like the mantle portion of the animal and would make that portion of its body around 75 feet long and 25' thick, with its arms adding another 100 feet to its total length (i.e. its "train"). Discounting its retracted feeding tentacles, this could be the largest squid ever witnessed. It certainly rivals the one from the Starkey incident (featured below).

The attack is typical of squid behavior, i.e. rush at the prey with arms at the ready, wrap it up, and then pull it toward its waiting beak. In this case, it collides with the *Pearl*, envelopes it, and then pulls it over and under. It may have believed the schooner was a whale.

I find the description of the squid's movements, which are described as "jerky" as it closes on the schooner, interesting. That sounds like a cephalopod propelling itself rapidly through the water by expelling seawater through its siphon. The fact that the incident was reported by multiple witnesses, with no indication of hoaxing, lends credibility to the account, despite its age.

It also suggests that these creatures are capable of capsizing fairly large boats and are more likely to approach sailing vessels. The quiet hulls of sailing ships are more likely to be mistaken for whales, the squid's natural prey. Also, whale oil was heavily in use for lanterns back then, and for other products as well. So the scent may have thrown it off.

---

[*] Sacramento Daily Union, Volume 47, Number 7277, 31 July 1874

Eighteenth century engraving of a giant squid attacking a schooner

Barque *Pauline* incident

January 18th, 1875. Although others have tried to dismiss this account as being nothing more than two amorous bull sperm whales, rolling around in the water and displaying their leviathan erections, reports from multiple eye witnesses, as well their sketches, suggest otherwise. In my opinion, the incident represents another instance of a monstrous squid being observed while feeding on a large sperm whale.

Per a story that ran in the *Illustrated London News* (November 20th, 1875), the captain's report read:

*"Captain Drevar, of the barque *Pauline*, bound with coals from Her Majesty's naval stores at Zanzibar, when in lat. 5 degrees 13 minutes. S., long. 35 degrees W., on July 8th last, observed three very large sperm whales, and one of them was gripped round the body, with two turns, by what appeared to be a huge serpent. Its back was of a darkish brown and its belly white, with an immense*

head and mouth, the latter always open; the head and tail had a length beyond the coils of about 30 feet; its girth was about 8 or 9 feet. Using its extremities as levers, the serpent whirled its victim round and round for about fifteen minutes, and then suddenly dragged the whale down to the bottom, head first. The other two whales, after attempting to release their companion, swam away upon its descent, exhibiting signs of the greatest terror.'*

In addition, the *Pauline's* captain and crew made the following official declaration before a stipendiary magistrate at the Dale Street Police Court in Liverpool.

We the undersigned, captain, officers, and crew of the barque Pauline, of London, do solemnly and sincerely declare that on July 8th, 1875, in latitude 5° 13', longitude 35° W., we observed three large sperm whales, and one of them was gripped round the body with two turns of what appeared to be a large serpent. The head and tail appeared to have a length beyond the coils of about thirty feet, and its girth eight or nine feet. The serpent whirled its victim round and round for about fifteen minutes, and then suddenly dragged the whale to the bottom, head first.**

George Drevar, Master
Horatio Thompson
Henderson Landello
Owen Baker
William Lewan

In addition, in a separate source that features a complete detailing from Captain Drevar, he mentions a sea monster "dragging over" a vessel in the Indian ocean. That must be a reference to the ill-fated schooner *Pearl*.***

---

* https://the-staxx.tumblr.com/post/6836497415/
on-november-20th-1875-the-illustrated-london

** https://www.futilitycloset.com/2007/10/23/monster-of-monsters/

*** https://www.yesteryearnews.com/sea-monster-stories

Part of his detailed report read:

*"Barque Pauline, July 8, 1875, latitude 5.13 N., longitude 35
W., Cape San Roque, north-east coast of Brazil, distance
20 miles at 11 a-m, the weather fine and clear, wind and
sea moderate, observed some black spots on the water, and
a whitish pillar some thirty-foot high above them. At the
first sight I took all to be breakers, as the sea was splashing up fountainlike about them, and the pinnacle rock,
bleached with the sun, but the pillar fell with a plash and
a similar one rose. They rose and fell alternately in quick
succession, and good glasses showed me it was a monster
sea serpent coiled twice round a large sperm whale. The
head and tail parts, each about thirty feet long, were acting as levers, twisting itself and its victim round with great
velocity. They sank out of sight every two minutes, coming
to the surface still revolving; and the struggles of the whale
and two other whales that were near frantic with excitement, made the sea in their vicinity like a boiling cauldron,
and a loud confused noise was distinctly heard."*

An embattled sperm whale, as seen from the *Pauline,*
from *Sea Monsters Unmasked, 1883*

215

In this instance, and after reading assorted portions of the reports, I believe it is possible to get a fairly accurate size estimation of the squid in question. After reading the abridged reports, I was under the impression that the "head and tail" of the monster was the mantle of a squid. At thirty feet or more in length (a portion of which would have been submerged) and eight or nine feet in width, that suggests a very large squid. Its head and mantle alone would have stretched forty feet in length – possibly more – and with the arms at least double that, overall. That is quite sufficient to drag even a huge sperm whale under.

However, the more detailed report suggests that the "head and tail parts" were rising up out of the water, repeatedly, and then falling. This is uncannily reminiscent of the *Delia* incident, wherein a whale was being attacked at the surface and its attacker raised its arms thirty feet into the sky, before raining repeated blows down upon the ensnared whale. This suggests a deliberate and instinctive tactic, like the kind Orcas or great white sharks do[*] when attempting to drown a sickly or wounded whale. The squid, perhaps lacking the sheer strength to drag the whale under and hold it there initially, resorted to inflicting hammering blows on its victim. This would gradually wear it down, while its beak (unseen by witnesses) tore at its prey's vulnerable abdominal region. The combination of pain, blood loss, and bludgeoning would eventually enable it to drag the hapless cetacean to its death.

---

[*] https://www.newsweek.com/great-white-shark-drown-whale-1517391

Mockup of a very large squid feeding on a sperm whale.
Based on the *Pauline* incident.

A.G. Starkey incident

WW2 (date unspecified). One of the most eerie monster squid encounters on record was experienced by a sailor named A.G. Starkey. During WWII, Starkey was stationed aboard a British Admiralty trawler, at that time lying off the Maldives Islands in the Indian Ocean. While on night watch duty (some accounts say he was fishing, others that he was working on the vessel's anti-submarine lights), he observed a squid alongside his boat that was every bit as large as his vessel!

"As I gazed, fascinated, a circle of green light glowed in my area of illumination. This green unwinking orb I suddenly realized was an eye. The surface of the water undulated with some

*strange disturbance. Gradually I realized that I was gazing at almost point-blank range at a huge squid."**

Understandably terrified by what he was seeing, Starkey began to back away from the squid. He kept going, until he eventually reached the other end of the ship. He realized, to his amazement, that the tail of the squid was at one end of the trawler and its tentacles were at the other.

The ship was over one hundred and seventy-five feet long.

I saw an old documentary on this and, if memory serves, Starkey stated he was smoking a cigarette when he saw the squid's trash-can-lid-sized eye peering up at him from the depths. If that's accurate, nightwatch duty makes the most sense. It also explains why he was alone at the time. Luckily for him, the squid wasn't interested in plucking a tiny biped off the trawler's deck for a late-night snack. Starkey stated that, after a time, the squid's enormous body suddenly expanded and it jetted away in complete silence. He was left standing there like a "James Bond" martini – shaken, but luckily unstirred.

I think it's likely that the vessel Starkey was on was, as some reports have indicated, using anti-submarine lights. Also known as diffused light camouflage, this was a system of active camouflage that utilized counter-illumination to allow a ship to match its background (the nighttime sky). By breaking up its silhouette, it reduced the chances of it being targeted by surfaced U-boats and Japanese submarines.**

If Starkey's trawler had this system, it might explain why the squid suddenly appeared beside his immobile vessel. Abyssal predators like *Architeuthis* and many other species use bioluminescence for both communication and as a means of finding food. Humboldt squid use flashes of light and changes in color to communicate with other members of their "pack", and the giant squid that was filmed in 2012 was lured into camera range

---

* S. Peter Dance, *Out of my Shell* (2005)

** https://en.wikipedia.org/wiki/Diffused_lighting_camouflage

via an artificial lightshow known as "Medusa". Starkey's monster was probably drawn to the trawler because it saw the glow of its hull lights and interpreted it as either a prospective mate or food.

Luckily for him, it realized its mistake and moved on.

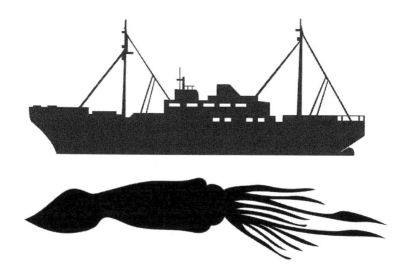

Mockup showing the size of the squid A.G. Starkey reported seeing beside his WW2 trawler

The Danger Point incident

October, 1966. Danger Point, Capetown, SA. According to a 1967 newspaper article, two lighthouse keepers watched for ninety minutes as, two hundred yards from shore, a giant squid launched a prolonged assault on a Southern right whale calf while its mother watched. The mother was, for some reason, unable to intervene, and could only circle and watch helplessly as the predator eventually drowned and then fed upon her infant.

Per the newspaper article, assistant lighthouse keeper Stephanus van Vuuren stated:

"We watched the fight through binoculars. The little whale would stay down for ten to twelve minutes, then come up. It would have just enough time to spout, just two or three seconds, then go down again. We saw it lashing with its tail in the water and the squid's tentacles rapped around its head. Each time the baby came up to breathe the mother surfaced with it and then went down with her infant. The little whale was only just able to reach the surface to spout. The squid never moved. Finally, we saw it come p for a second, blow, then go down. We never saw it again . . ."

A horrific story. According to the newspaper, the calf was only seven feet long, with the squid's arms estimated at six feet. However, it appears that the keeper's estimate through his binoculars was off. Per Wikipedia, right whale calves range between 4-6 meters at birth (13-20 feet). This means the calf was far larger than the witnesses thought, hence the squid was bigger too. It could've been two or three times as large, meaning an *Architeuthis* with arms roughly from eleven to seventeen feet in length. That would put the entire animal somewhere between twenty-five and thirty-five feet in length (sans feeding tentacles).

A squid that size is nothing spectacular, but still plenty big enough to kill. And the incident proves that giant squid can and do target whales as prey, and that they are both merciless and unrelenting once they've latched onto their target (the *Pauline* and *Delia* incidents bear this out). A ninety-minute struggle also suggests tremendous tenacity on the part of the cephalopod, which, of course, has a huge advantage as it has no problem breathing. It only has to hold on and use its siphon to keep pulling its air-breathing victim beneath the surface (possibly feeding on it at the same time).

---

* *The Gettysburg Times*, March 16th, 1967

Sadly, with the mother and a third whale apparently unable to assist, the combination of fatigue and blood loss meant it was only a matter of time.

There's never a pod of calamari-loving Orcas around when you need one.

PAGE TWO

WHALE BEATEN BY GIANT SQUID

CAPE TOWN, South Africa (AP) —The large swells of the normally choppy sea around the Cape of Storms were suddenly disturbed at Danger Point on a quiet afternoon.

About 200 yards offshore from the scenic Cape Town beach a life-and-death duel was being fought between a giant squid and a seven-foot Southern Right calf whale.

The baby whale's mother circled helpless near the death struggle as the squid slowly drowned the calf, its six-foot-long tentacles clamped tightly around its head.

For 90 minutes lighthouse keepers at Danger Point watched the little whale battle gamely, visibly weakening under the pressure of the squid.

Later a third whale joined the cow, but could do nothing to end the battle. Meantime the calf continued to drown, slowly, as it surfaced less and less frequently for air.

Assistant lighthouse keeper Ste-

Assistant lighthouse keeper Stephanus van Vuuren said afterwards: "We watched the fight through binoculars. The little whale would stay down for 10 to 12 minutes, then come up. It would just have enough time to spout, just two or three seconds, then go down again.

"We saw it lashing with its tail in the water and the squid's tentacles wrapped around its head. Each time the baby came up to breathe, the mother whale surfaced with it and then went down with her infant.

"The little whale was only just able to reach the surface to spout. The squid never moved. Finally we saw it come up for a second, blow, then go down. We never saw it again. . . ."

Details of squid attack article from *The Gettysburg Times*

Original article in *The Gettysburg Times*, March 16th, 1967

USS Stein incident

In 1978, the 438-foot, 4,207-ton *Knox*-class destroyer escort *USS Stein* (DE-1065) became the only U.S. warship to have suffered a confirmed mega-squid attack. Shortly after leaving port, the Stein's sonar went inoperative. Effectively blind, the ship was forced to return to San Diego to affect repairs. An examination of its AN/SQS-26 sonar dome revealed numerous slashes in its "NO-FOUL" rubber coating. Embedded in these slashes were broken-off claws, similar to the tiny "teeth" that line the rims of the suckers of many types of squid. However, these hook-like squid claws came from an unknown species and were, according to reports, nearly five times the size of those on the suckers of any known specimen.[*] That suggests a giant squid with a head and mantle *alone* that measured 100 feet in length.

---

[*] *Johnson, C. Scott (August 1978). "Sea Creatures and the Problem of Equipment Damage".*

Knox-class destroyer escort *USS Stein* (DE-1065). Image credit: National
Archives (public domain)

As a reference, let's examine this U.S. Navy public domain
image of the same AN/SQS-26 sonar dome being installed
on the destroyer *USS Willis A. Lee* back in 1961. According to
Wikipedia:

*The AN/SQS-26 weighed 27,215 kg (59,999 lb). It could be oper-
ated as a passive sonar on the 1.5 kHz frequency or as an active
sonar at 3-4 kHz. Its maximum output was 240 kW and it had a
range from 18 to 64 km (11 to 40 mi). It had direct path, bottom
reflected, passive and convergence zone (CZ) capabilities.*

It is a known fact that individual sperm whales consume over one ton of squid per day*. At lengths that can exceed sixty feet, they are the giant squid's primary predator. They also use focused echolocation clicks to target their prey. A sperm whale's typical sonar clicks range from 10 Hz to 30 kHz. Thus, the sonar dome used on destroyers like the *USS Stein* emitted sonar in the same ranges that the whales do**. In fact, the *Stein*'s active sonar frequencies were probably similar to the higher ranges a sperm whale uses when focusing on a potential meal.

A cursory examination of the sonar dome on the *Willis A. Lee* shows that, in terms of shape, it could easily be mistaken for the head of a sperm whale. A very large one.

---

* https://www.nature.com/articles/srep45517

** https://www.globalsecurity.org/military/systems/ship/systems/an-sqs-23.htm

I did some digging, and found that the previous model AN/SQS-23 had a transducer diameter of over twenty feet* and the SQS-26 was even bigger. Although I couldn't find exact stats for the latter, based on the photo, I'm betting that sonar array is at least twenty-five feet across. There hasn't been a sperm whale in the history of the world that had a head that wide; at least that I know of. But for an immense squid accustomed to fearing nothing, the *Stein*'s shadow passing over it, coupled with the shape of the destroyer's bow and the active sonar it was emitting, probably convinced it that it was about to be attacked by its hereditary enemy.

An enemy that was big enough to kill and eat it.

Squid can be incredibly aggressive, and there are multiple reports of them attacking ships much bigger than themselves**. The *Stein* squid must have felt predation was imminent and gone into attack mode. It lashed out, fastening its tentacles onto the sonar dome of the destroyer and shredding it. Within seconds, it realized its mistake and disengaged, but not before inflicting serious damage on a steel warship many times its mass.

Mockup of the *USS Stein* showing possible sizes for its attacker.
Image credit: the author.

---

* https://en.wikipedia.org/wiki/Cephalopod_attack
**

I did some hardcore number crunching and came up with the above comparison of the 438' *USS Stein* and the mollusk that attacked it. We know that the squid sucker claws found in the sonar dome's covering were from an unknown species. This overwhelmingly suggests that *Architeuthis dux* is not the largest squid out there (nor the Colossal squid, *Mesonychoteuthis hamiltoni*).

I based my mockup on two possibilities. The first is that the destroyer's attacker was built like the giant squid. I scaled up that one (shown in gray) based on the largest documented example: the November 2, 1877 specimen found in Thimble Tickle Bay, Newfoundland. Once regarded by *Guinness* as the world's largest invertebrate, it had a head and mantle length of 20'. This suggested an animal with a total body length of around 100 feet and an LOA around twice that.

The second possibility (shown in black), and the one that I believe to be most likely, is that the squids that attacked the *Stein* and the schooner *Pearl*, and the one that surfaced alongside Starkey's WW2 trawler, were all of the same species. It makes sense. The destroyer may well have encountered an unknown genus, and a 175-foot animal like Starkey reported is the right size to do the job. Not to mention, it's in the same ballpark, size-wise, as my scaled-up *Architeuthis*.

But why would a squid attack a destroyer?

Even the biggest of squid start off small. And juveniles of this unknown species undoubtedly fall prey to sperm whales. Hence, the species undoubtedly views the whale as its enemy; even when it's big enough to reverse roles and becomes the whale's predator. As I said previously, the squid probably thought the ship's sonar dome was the head of a huge sperm whale, preparing to attack it. But it was not expecting a 438' destroyer to be attached to said head. Once it realized its mistake it broke off its assault.

Geronimo trimaran incident

January, 2003. While competing in, ironically enough, the round-the-world *Jules Verne Trophy*, the crew of the trimaran yacht *Geronimo* suddenly found themselves besieged by a giant squid. The *Geronimo*, a 22-ton, 110.9-foot triple-hulled sailing vessel was off the coast of Gibraltar when its 24-knots speed suddenly plummeted to 11 knots (27.6 to 12.65 mph). A hungry squid had attacked the boat and affixed itself to the stern region.

Veteran yachtsman Didier Ragot stated:

"It was a giant squid. The tentacles were as thick as my arms plus the waterproofs. Amazing! To begin with it was jammed between the top of the rudder blade and the hull and then it sent two of its tentacles down to the base of the rudder blade and grasped it right the way around at fence level. I saw it astern after it had let go, and I reckon it was about 10 meters long: absolutely enormous. It's the first time I've ever seen one so big: it shook the whole boat and it was rather worrying at the time. If it had managed to climb on board, we'd have had to offer it lunch or something to keep it from lunching on us.

We were all ready to do battle with boathooks and knives, but as soon as we slowed the boat down, it obviously decided that it would be better to let us go while it had the chance and that's exactly what it did. Our first concern was whether or not it had damaged the boat. We slowed the boat immediately to check for damage, but luckily, the only problem was a small amount of water in the bearings."[*]

---

[*] https://www.sailing.org/news/13074.php#.X6NCR1B7k2x

A fantastic and hair-raising encounter, to be sure. After examining all the facts, I believe the squid looked up and saw *Geronimo*'s three hulls passing over it at the surface and assumed it was witnessing a trio of blue or finback whales swimming together in a pod. The long, slender shapes of the trimaran's hulls would have contributed to this, as would the fact that the vessel was moving silently under sail power. It saw its opportunity to score a meal and took its shot. This is borne up by the fact that it attacked the yacht's rudder, most likely believing it to be its prey's flukes. Its attack technique was similar to that of the Danger Point attack on a right whale calf. It held on and tried to use its mass and waterjet propulsion to drag its victim down.

In terms of size, the squid that did this would have had to have been bigger than the ten meters (32.7 feet) quoted. At least, in terms of overall length. The image below shows the remains of a giant squid that washed ashore in Ranheim, Norway, on October 2, 1954. Including the long feeding tentacles, it mea-sured 9.24 meters overall (just over 30 feet).

Ragot stated that the attacking squid's arms were as thick as his arms plus his protective waterproof jacket, and another yachtsman, Olivier de Kersauson stated that he saw one of the squid's tentacles through a porthole and that it was thicker than his leg. He estimated its size at seven or eight meters (22 to 26 feet).* I believe that, when these two men estimated its size, they were referring to the squid's body, its tentacles not included.

---

* http://news.bbc.co.uk/2/hi/science/nature/2661691.stm

Image credit: NYNU Museum of Natural History and Archaeology

That has to be the case. Per the witnesses, the cephalopod that assaulted *Geronimo* had arms that were three or four times as thick as the Norway specimen show above. Scaling up, if we tripled the Norway specimen in size (its mantle-only length sans the head portion was 1.79 meters or nearly six feet) its total body length without arms would be around twenty-four feet and its overall length would be around fifty feet. Including the two long feeding tentacles it could stretch anywhere from seventy-five to ninety feet (tentacle lengths vary greatly among individuals). That would be big enough to slow a yacht the size of *Geronimo* and, potentially, big enough to tackle an adult fin-back whale – most likely the squid's intended target.

From this incident we can infer that:

1. Huge squid are capable of attacking large boats
2. Unpowered vessels (either sailing or drifting) are more likely to be targeted
3. The evidence once again suggests the largest squid can and do target whales as prey

Squid Size Chart

Theoretical squid size chart. 1: an est. 60' specimen (90'+ including the extended feeding tentacles). 2: an est. 90' squid (sans feeding tentacles) – potentially the size of the animal involved in the *Delia* and *Pauline* whale attacks. 3: a squid in the 175' range – a size appropriate for the *Pearl*, *USS Stein*, and A.G. Starkey incidents. 4: a sperm whale in the 85' range (based on Soviet whaling records). 5: a post-whaling sperm whale in the 60' range. 6: the largest Orca recorded at 32'. 7: a record size blue whale.

Giant squid attacking a boat. Public domain image.

Whale Attacked by "Extinct" Marine Reptile?

The old Gods were creatures to be feared.

Back when I was hunkering down to write the first *Kronos Rising* novel, that thought was foremost in my mind. I had to do a lot of research on the marine reptiles of the Mesozoic – the mighty mosasaurs and pliosaurs that once ruled Earth's oceans in particular.

It was fascinating stuff, learning the physiology and feeding habits of the world's greatest predators, and safe. I was reading about them, not studying them firsthand. It wasn't like I had a choice. After all, they're all dead and gone. There's nothing left but fossils.

At least, that's what I always believed. That is, until my book research started uncovering eye witness statements like this one from World War I, where the German submarine U28, while operating in the North Atlantic under the command of Captain Freiherr Georg von Forstner, torpedoed the British steamer *Iberian*. His report reads as follows[*]:

> *"On July 30, 1915, our U-28 torpedoed the British steamer Iberian, which was carrying a rich cargo (trucks and jeeps primarily) across the North Atlantic. The steamer sank so swiftly that its bow stuck up almost vertically into the air. Moments later the hull of the Iberian disappeared.*

---

[*] excerpt from *In the Wake of the Sea Serpents*, by Bernard Huevelmans

The wreckage remained beneath the water for approximately twenty-five seconds, at a depth that was clearly impossible to assess, when suddenly there was a violent explosion, which shot pieces of debris — among them a gigantic aquatic animal — out of the water to a height of approximately eighty feet.

At that moment I had with me in the conning tower six of my officers of the watch, including the chief engineer, the navigator, and the helmsman. Simultaneously we all drew one another's attention to this wonder of the seas, which was writhing and struggling among the debris.

We were unable to identify the creature, but all of us agreed that it resembled an aquatic crocodile, which was about 60-feet long, with four limbs resembling large webbed feet, a long, pointed tail and a head which also tapered to a point. Unfortunately, we were not able to take a photograph, for the animal sank out of sight after ten or fifteen seconds."

If you've read *Kronos Rising*, you probably recognize that quote.

Over the course of writing my novel, I uncovered many more (and some far more recent) reports and sightings of creatures that bore an eerie resemblance to supposedly extinct marine predators. Being a relatively stolid individual, however, I took such things in stride. Although the creative in me longed for these reports to turn out to be factual, the realist in me was inclined to dismiss them as either simple misidentifications of existing species or the byproduct of alcohol consumption, combined with overactive imaginations.

Things have certainly changed since then.

There is a Facebook fan page for the *Kronos Rising* series, and on that page my admins and I actively interact with readers. One of the posts that is sometimes featured is titled,

"Prop or Predator". In it, I feature photos of whales or sharks that are sporting injuries. I encourage readers to voice their opinions as to what was responsible for the damage. Was the huge hunk taken out of that unfortunate humpback's flukes caused by a ship's propeller or a killer whale attack? If neither makes sense, is it possible something far more sinister was responsible?

It's fun for my readers, and I enjoy the back and forth. Recently, I came across a series of photographs of a beached whale that, at first glance, looked like many of the others I've posted. When I looked closely at one photo, however, I saw something that gave me pause. And when I studied it in detail, I became startled.

On August 13th, 2012, a 65-foot finback whale ended up stranded on the beach off the St. Austell coast of England. This was documented by both still pictures and film footage. According to the reports, the whale swam into the shallows and remained there until the receding tide left it stranded. Despite rescue efforts, the whale – which was reported as malnourished, extremely distressed, and sporting injuries to its face and eye – died shortly thereafter.

What struck me as odd, and what nobody seems to have paid attention to, are the wounds on the whale's face. There are a series of deep punctures running along the right side of its lower jaw that are visible in many of the pictures. The punctures are evenly spaced and run in a straight line, then curve around to form an elongated U-shaped pattern. Due to copyright issues, the photos aren't included here. But a simple Google search will readily produce them.

When I saw this wound pattern, I was taken aback. Novelist or no, I'm not given to flights of fantasy. I prefer to deal with reality. I like empirical evidence – real, physical stuff that I can touch, test, and relate to. If you show me a really good Sasquatch footprint, for example, I'll be interested. If you show me where one chomped down on your shoulder, however, I'll be intrigued.

It's a lot harder to fake a bite mark than it is a footprint. And when I looked at the wound pattern on the finback whale's face, I found myself coming to an unexpected conclusion.

It looks like a bite mark.

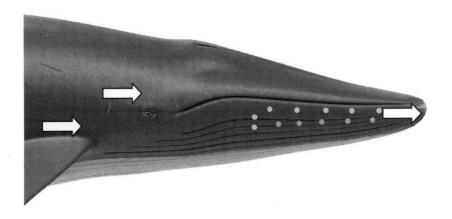

Reconstruction of the stranded finback whale's head with puncture marks indicated with white and gray dots. Areas of missing tissue are indicated by arrows.

Based on the photographs, it appears that something huge, with crocodile-shaped jaws lined with teeth, attacked the finback. It sounds insane, but then, crazy things happen all the time.

Is it possible? Is there some other explanation?

Frankly, I can't think of one. It's not a shark bite, nor that of a sperm whale (not that they feed on other whales, anyway). Rocks or rebar from ruptured pilings don't make organized punctures like that, and I just can't picture someone coming down to the beach with an oversized pickaxe while crowds are gathered and cameras rolling, and whacking away at the poor, beached whale in such a precise manner without getting spotted.

Not to mention, even stranded in the shallows, I don't think the whale would have been very receptive.

The wounds aren't bleeding. That means they're not fresh. If the whale had been rolling around on sharp stones in the shallows, it would be bleeding. Moreover, there is video footage of the whale and you can see there are no stones around it, just sand.

Of course, without examining the whale's corpse and the other side of its jaw in particular, it's impossible to say with any degree of certainty. However, barring some unforeseen explanation coming to light, I'm inclined to stand by my theory. Think about it: A large cetacean: wounded, distressed, and malnourished, basically committed suicide by beaching itself. That's what happened. The whale swam into the shallows and remained there, even as the tide went out, allowing itself to become stranded – a certain death.

Why would a whale do that?

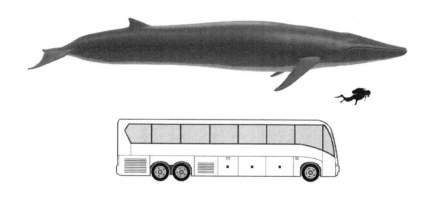

Recreation of a healthy 65' finback whale with a diver
and bus for comparison.

As a novelist who specializes in marine terror, the motivator that automatically comes to mind is fear. I would imagine a slow death on a beach from suffocation would be infinitely preferable to being torn apart and devoured by a monstrous predator. It would be like choosing between sitting in a closed garage with the car engine running and being eaten alive by a hungry crocodile. Which would you prefer?

Although it's impossible to prove this, I'm going to approach this from a "what if?" angle. What if I'm correct in my interpretation? Then the next question is: 'How would such an attack have taken place?'

The storyteller in me once again springs to the fore. Per force, there are myriad possibilities. If it is a bite mark, then based on the physical evidence and what we know, I can make an educated guess as to what transpired. The finback whale may have been attacked out at sea, by something along the lines of an enormous mosasaur or pliosaur.

Note: the fossil record supports the potential for such a predator in the exact same region. The Weymouth Bay pliosaur (also known as *Pliosaurus kevani*), whose skull is on display in the Dorset County Museum in Dorchester, had a tooth-lined skull measuring nearly eight feet in length, with the animal itself calculated at nearly forty.

Going by the Getty images online – in particular the one where rescue workers are surrounding the finback's head, you can see the portion of the whale's lower jaw that was affected by the punctures measures about six feet. Given that the punctures are shallower and more ragged closer to the tip of the whale's jaw (and also taking into account the whale's bullet-shaped head, which would have resulted in more scrapes and less punctures if that portion of its face was inside a predator's wide-open mouth), if they were, indeed, caused by teeth, the attacker would've had to have had a substantial gape.

Assuming that they are tooth punctures, and using a lateral view of the Weymouth Bay pliosaur's skull as a point of reference, I estimate the jaws of the creature that attacked the finback measured around ten feet in length. With a five-to-one ratio of skull to body, that equates to a pliosaur around fifty feet in length or a mosasaur over sixty feet – in the size range of the animal U-Boat Captain von Forstner spotted in 1915.

The news reports also state that the whale was very malnourished, extremely distressed, and had numerous injuries, including scrapes and scratches and wounds around its eye, as can be seen in the images. In the video, you can hear one of the rescue workers stating that divers reported the animal had also suffered abdominal wounds (note, photos or footage of these abdominal wounds was never shown).

I find it odd that an elite dive team showed up there. Is that the norm for strandings? I've never heard of it happening elsewhere.

Closeup of a beached finback whale. Note its emaciated condition.

Again, assuming we're dealing with something attacking the finback, and knowing how modern ambush predators like white sharks make a living, I would venture that the whale was initially attacked from below. That makes sense, as it avoids a defensive fluke strike. Also, attacking the whale's face – its toughest, boniest point, would have been far less productive. So, an abdominal strike – designed to cause it to bleed out and die – would be the best way to go.

Another question that begs addressing: Was the whale already malnourished when it was attacked? It's quite possible. Predators often zero weak and injured animals, and a healthy adult finback would be a strong and swift opponent – one tough to drag down, especially for a lone assailant.

On the other hand, if the initial attack had been unsuccessful, the whale's attacker may have simply kept after it, like a Komodo dragon that delivers a deadly bite and then waits for its prey to expire. The aggressor may have pursued the wounded whale and repeatedly harried it, with the goal of preventing it from feeding or resting until it was so drained and exhausted it was unable to fight back – an easy kill.

Again, these are all just guesses. One thing that is more certain is that the whale, knowing it was doomed, took to the shallows to die. Its pursuer, most likely a crafty hunter that shies away from human beings and their noisy ships, might have taken steps to prevent this. It is at this point that I imagine it attacked the finback head-on, possibly trying to seize it by the throat. The whale may have sacrificed its face to save its throat and its attacker, now locked onto it, could have attempted to wrestle it down, hoping to drown it or kill it outright.

The damage to the whale's face lends credence to such a possibility; the loss of tissue around its eye may have happened as the two titans struggled back and forth, dragging their way along the rough sea floor with the whale fighting for its life.

In such a scenario, the finback, battling with the strength of desperation, may have broken free from its reptilian adversary and fled for the shallows. With its pursuer waiting hungrily in the distance, the exhausted and terrified cetacean resolved to remain there to die, rather than facing what waited for it in the deep.

I have attached a sketch which shows how I believe the finback may have sustained the pattern of puncture wounds to its face, a pattern similar to both the jaw structure and arsenal of spiked teeth found in the mandibles of *Pliosaurus kevani*. It shows both side and top views, illustrating how such an attack may have inflicted the injuries the whale had.

As is so often the case; without members of the scientific community having an opportunity to examine the long-gone carcass of the finback for additional clues, we may never know the truth.

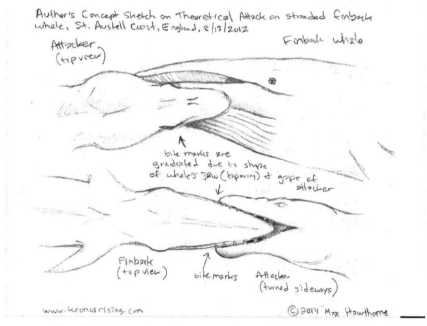

Sketch by the author, demonstrating a possible explanation
for the wounds on the whale's face.

Many people believe that "extinct" creatures still roam the forests and oceans of the world. Whether it's the Yeti, Champ, or Nessie, the legends of these creatures remain, often with regular sightings to bolster them. In the past, I looked at these assorted reports from a cautious, albeit hopeful perspective

– the viewpoint of a writer with a passion for such things who would like to believe in them, but is hesitant to say he does. Now, the situation seems a bit different. Before, all that existed were aged anecdotal reports and eye witness accounts. Now, we may have something tangible.

Put another way, if this book has shown us anything, it's that our oceans may be a far more diverse (and harrowing) place than any of us realize. And if these creatures – these great, scaly titans of prehistory – are still out there, lurking in the ocean depths, and (wisely) avoiding us like the plague, we need to find them. We need to study them, learn from them, and most importantly, we need to protect them. Because if the remnants of a race of macropredators that once shared our planet with the dinosaurs are still alive, they are the greatest survivors in the history of the world.

They are the true Lords of the Deep.

And they sure as hell deserve our respect.

Young Bigfoot Swimming
in Connecticut Lake?

A lthough I've investigated numerous cryptids and even seen a few, as an author whose novels center around the possibilities of prehistoric marine life surviving to the present, and whose contributions to paleontology focus primarily on marine reptiles, cryptids like Bigfoot are, admittedly, outside my area of expertise. That said, I *did* have a sighting of my own of some sort of hairy "biped" while I was fishing one day.

In the interest of being forthcoming, I've included it here.

The sighting took place during a week-long vacation at my family's then lake house in Danbury, Connecticut. Our home overlooked scenic Candlewood lake, known for its lush surroundings, dense forests, quaint homes, and spectacular boating, sail-boating, and fishing.

Ten miles from Danbury, and located in the town of New Fairfield, is Squantz Pond State Park. It is centered around 288-acre Squantz pond, which connects via a causeway to Candlewood Lake, proper. I've fished Squantz many times: from shore, from canoes, and from my boat. The fishing is good and the lake is deep, approaching fifty feet in places. The waters of Squantz tend to be cold and are often murky, and there have been many drownings.

From 1996 to 2011, fifteen people are confirmed to have drowned in the lake[*], more than at any other state park. There have also been occurrences where someone was reported to

---

[*] https://en.wikipedia.org/wiki/Squantz_Pond_State_Park

have disappeared in the water, only to have the incident written off as a false alarm.* For the record, having frequented the park many times, it is impossible to keep track of every person that arrives there by boat, bicycle, hiking in, etc.

For the record, Connecticut is not without its reports of Bigfoot-like creatures. Tales of the "Winstead Wildman" go back to 1895, where a townsman was out picking blueberries when he was interrupted by a hair-covered, muscular creature six feet in height. The Wildman was seen by several individuals. Then it disappeared.

It reappeared nearly eighty years later in 1972, near Crystal Lake Reservoir, where it was described as being eight feet tall, and again in 1974 near Rugg Brook Reservoir, where two couples who parked there at night were terrorized by a "six-foot, 300-pound creature covered with dark-colored hair".** Lastly, in 2005, Bristol, CT had a report of a smallish Sasquatch-type creature standing 5.5 feet in height.***

The woods around Squantz pond are thick with heavy timber and huge stones.

* https://www.nbcconnecticut.com/news/local/
police-search-squantz-pond-for-missing-swimmer/1888638/

** http://www.damnedct.com/the-winsted-wildman/

*** http://www.bigfootencounters.com/sbs/hartford2005.htm

Interestingly, almost all of these sightings took place near bodies of freshwater. Mine did too.

I'd be lying if I said I knew the date or even the year of my sighting. I'm fairly sure I know which girl I was dating at the time, so it was probably the summer of either 1993 or 1994. I remember I was gainfully unemployed at the time, so taking a week or two to go up to CT to fish was not a problem.

I also know that it was definitely a weekday, and I remember it had rained the night before. It was still cloudy and overcast when my brothers and I got to Squantz. It was early, maybe six AM on a guess, and the lake was flat calm and deserted. Weekdays there were far better for fishing than weekends, as there were no Jet Skis or motorboats. And a weekday, right after the sun came up, was prime time. The fish would be active, and the poor bastards that had to go to work were still asleep.

We shore fished that day, using live minnows as bait. We parked in the nearby lot and hoofed it over to the causeway that separated Squantz pond from Candlewood lake (technically, Squantz is part of Candlewood). The causeway is a manmade two-lane road that separates the two lakes. It is elevated and rests on a large mound of rocks that slope down to the water on either side. You can fish from the rocks, although the footing can be treacherous. At the center of the rockpile, and on either side, is a submerged concrete tunnel that allows fish and wildlife to travel back and forth between the two bodies of water. I've seen many animals use it.

My brothers and I had fished the Squantz side of the causeway for a good thirty minutes without a bite. They became bored and decided to cross the road (taking the cooler with all the food and drinks with them, as I recall) and fish the Candlewood side. I stayed put, confident that the wriggling minnows I had suspended beneath my two bobbers would eventually bring me a fish.

Perhaps fifteen minutes later, I saw something swimming toward me. It was maybe 150 feet away when I first spotted it. I saw what I believe was a head. It bobbed to the surface, disappeared, reappeared, and then submerged again. I was looking down at it from an elevated position, and I could sort of see it, despite the clouded water. The "head" – and I'm sure that what I saw was its head, as it was swimming straight toward me – was like a bowling ball, round and wet, and it appeared to be covered with thick, reddish-brown hair. I could see the top of its head as it repeatedly came to the surface, pushing water as it did. It would bob to the surface, stay there for a second or so, and then submerge again, only to reappear twenty to thirty feet closer.

By the time it got to within perhaps thirty yards, I could see the general shape of its body. It was long, perhaps five feet in length. I knew it was too big to be a beaver (although the color was similar) and far too large to be a muskrat. I was about to write it off as a water-loving Irish setter, when it surfaced again, only fifty feet away. At this point, I saw the roundness of (what I assume was) the crown of its head. At this point, I stood up to try and see it more clearly. I don't know if it became aware of me or not – I probably dislodged a few rocks – but it submerged immediately.

That was the weirdest part. The creature (for want of a better term) was not doing a front crawl while swimming. In fact, it looked like it was using its whole body to swim, sort of like a kicking motion with its legs together. But as it dove, its left arm broke the surface, and I got a clear look at what was a decidedly humanish upper arm, elbow, and forearm. It was about the size of my arm (mind you, I was a passionate weightlifter at the time, and had seventeen-inch 'guns') but covered with long, reddish-brown hair. You could see the hair hanging down, with water streaming from it as it lifted up.

I did a double-take, and blinked a few times to make sure I hadn't imagined things. Although I couldn't see it clearly, from the shadowy disturbance in the water at the base of the rock pile, I could tell the "hairy red thing" (as I mentally referred to it) had just passed into the underwater tunnel that separated Squantz from Candlewood. I opened the bails on both my rods and left them, then scrambled up the rocks and across the road to the other side, where my brothers were busy chatting away and catching nothing.

I told them that I'd just seen something hairy swim past me and go under the causeway. When I told them it had an elbow, I got the anticipatory guffaws and abuse. And then some.

Still, we stood there watching, waiting to see if the creature would show itself. It didn't. There were a lot of lily pads on the left shoreline, adjacent to the causeway. I was fairly sure I saw a disturbance move through them, but I suppose that could've been a big bass or one of any number of other lake inhabitants.

Are there Bigfoot reports in that exact area? Yes. For the life of me, I can't find the info, but I came across a newspaper report online from the Danbury region, one that went back to the early 1900s. In it, fishermen reported seeing a "hairy wild child" by the lake and/or in it.

So, was it a young Bigfoot? I have no idea. Anything is possible. All I can tell you is what I saw was not a deer, bear, or beaver. Nor was it a mountain lion. It had a dome-shaped head (the top at least) and was an adept and cautious swimmer – one that preferred to spend most of its time submerged. It was also smart enough to conceal itself once it realized it was being observed.

Beyond that, it's anyone's guess. All I know for sure is that, between the drownings and what I witnessed, I've lost any desire to swim in Squantz pond ever again.

A vista view of Squantz Pond.
The causeway mentioned in the sighting is to the right.

Mothman or Something Else?

Given the thousands of hours I've spent on boats, fishing both fresh and saltwater, one would expect any cryptid sightings I experienced to be of the aquatic variety. You know, some sort of Loch Ness monster or Kraken type encounter where said beastie attacks the boat, resulting in me pushing the charter captain or mate in its way so they get eaten instead of me.

I'm kidding. Sort of.

Instead, however, the two most astonishing, up-close-and-personal encounters I've had (I'm discounting the swimming juvenile Sasquatch – if that's what it was – as it was a rather ambiguous encounter) were with terrestrial creatures. They were both things of myth and legend that, in the "real world" aren't supposed to exist.

Apparently, nobody told them that.

The first of these took place fairly recently. It was November 22, 2016, to be exact. I know the date because after it happened, I stumbled into the house and, among other things, made a sketch of what we'd seen, complete with the date on it.

I say *we* because it wasn't just myself. My (then) seven-year-old daughter was with me in the truck.

It was around 6:30 PM that Tuesday, when Ava and I encountered the creature. I'd picked her up at aftercare around 5:50 PM and we'd swung by our local Wawa (a well-known convenience store chain) to grab some dinner, before heading home. It was cold – mid to upper 30s, as memory serves – and fairly windy. There was some snow flurrying going on, but between the swirling wind and temps that were not quite freezing, nothing was sticking.

Visibility was poor, however, and it made for slick road conditions. As a result, I was extra cautious as we worked our way toward the house.

The sighting took place surprisingly close to home. I should point out that, if this was a woodland creature, it makes sense that we saw it. We live in a heavily wooded area, with the forest literally a stone's throw away. Whitetail deer, wild turkeys, raccoons, groundhogs, and opossum are common, along with raptors ranging from red-tailed hawks to an occasional American eagle. Several times, I've had groups of enormous mule deer right behind the house. And one winter, after Ava had gotten on the school bus, I found a perfect path of four-inch-wide cat tracks traveling from the street into our yard, and traversing it completely until they disappeared into the woods out back.

They say there are no mountain lions in PA.

I beg to differ.

As we were driving along a dark and deserted street, working our way along, the flurries continued to twirl around with the wind's powerful gusts. It was indeed a "blustery eve", as someone I know put it. Although there didn't seem to be anyone around (it was a school night and suppertime), the risk of a child running out in front of one's vehicle is always there and, as a result, I remained on high alert as we continued on.

Suddenly, perhaps fifty feet away from us, I saw something dark in the middle of the road, directly ahead. It was laying on the ground and silhouetted by my headlights. Size-wise, I'd estimate it was perhaps six inches wide and two to three inches high. I assumed it was a box or a piece of debris and reflexively said aloud, "Uh, oh. We've got something in the road ahead."

At this point, Ava leaned sideways in her car seat so she could see (her seat was situated behind the front passenger seat). As a result, she got almost as good a look at what we encountered as I did.

Actually, with her 20/10 eyesight, maybe better.

Still assuming that the object was a piece of debris, I altered course slightly so that my SUV's wheels would straddle it instead of running over it. It could've been a box of nails, for all I knew, and I had no desire to get a flat tire. At this point, I was going fairly slowly; I would say probably slow jogging speed.

By the time we were thirty feet from the object, I slowed to a crawl.

The "object" had started to move.

At this point, I still believed I was looking at a piece of trash or something – a discarded box, most likely. I told myself that a loose "flap" from one end of the supposed box, fluttering in the wind, explained the sudden movement.

A second later, I realized what I was looking at was no box.

I came to a full stop at this point, with the thing on the ground perhaps twenty feet from my headlights. It was brightly illuminated and as it looked up (yes, *it* looked up) I realized what I was staring at was the head of some sort of creature.

What happened next took place over a period of just ten or fifteen seconds. But in my mind, it lasted an eternity.

I saw a face of some kind, looking up at me. In the headlights it appeared to be a dark gray in color. The creature's head was about the size of an apple. It had black eyes with no visible whites, and a wide-open mouth that also appeared black.

My initial (and admittedly shocked) reaction was: *Is that some kind of animal?*

It looked very odd, and my brain fast-forwarded through every creature I could think of, starting with those known from North America and then expanding outward. This was none of those. In terms of color and size, it reminded me of the *Homunculus* from the movie, *The Golden Voyage of Sinbad*. The skin on its face was smooth and it had some sort of scraggly hair around it, almost like a mane. I could also tell that it was *very* upset. Its mouth was wide open, suggesting it was either screaming or snarling at us, although with my SUV's doors closed, we obviously couldn't hear it.

Author's sketch of the face of the creature as it raised its
head up off the ground.

I couldn't blame it. I imagine with 5,000 pounds of truck bearing down on it, high-beams blazing, as it lay in the middle of a freezing street, it was more than a little frightened.

At this point, I was frozen in place. The creature was about ten feet from my headlights and I just stared at it, not sure what to do. It started pushing itself upright with what I assume were arms, until it reached a height of maybe a foot or so.

I try to avoid using expletives around my child – good parenting and what not – but as this thing glared at me, I couldn't help it.

Just as the words, "What the *hell* is *that?*" leapt from my mouth, the thing sprang up. And when I say "sprang up", it leapt straight into the air and stayed there.

It was then that I realized it had wings.

It was hovering about eye level with myself, so perhaps six feet off the ground. It was looking right at me, and Ava was looking right at it. She pointed at it and, in response to what was meant to be a rhetorical question, shouted, "It's a fairy, daddy! It's a fairy!"

For a second or two more, the creature remained suspended in front of my truck. I could see its wings plainly. There were two sets, matched pairs. They were like the wings of a dragonfly; except they didn't have the same shape. Both sets were the same size and they looked like elongated ovals, rounded at the tips. I could see them plainly, practically luminescent in my headlights' glare. They vibrated like a hummingbird's wings, allowing it to hold position.

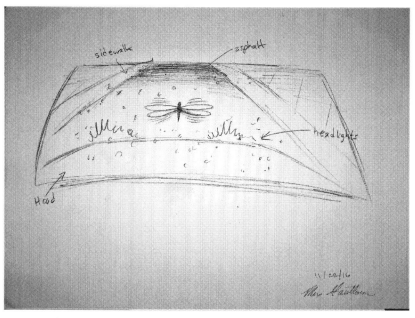

Author's drawing of the creature he and his daughter saw,
suspended in front of his headlights.

I should point out that the creature looked entirely different as it hovered there. Its body, once gray, now had a whitish or silvery look to it – it was almost ghostlike or ethereal – like it had somehow recharged itself and was showing its true form. Its wings were completely clear, and if it hadn't been so brightly illuminated, I don't think I would've seen them.

In retrospect, I think it was hurt when we came across it. Perhaps it had been blinded by the flying snow and struck a powerline or something, then crash-landed onto the street. Judging by how its appearance had altered, I suspect it was able to camouflage itself. It may have initially taken on the color of the asphalt, hence its grayish appearance. Once it had gathered itself, however, and sprang up, it looked nothing like that.

It was dazzling, almost angelic.

Still airborne, the baleful stare the creature was giving me was interrupted by my daughter. When she shouted and pointed at it, she drew its attention to herself. I don't know if the realization there was another person there alarmed it, or perhaps it saw a pointed finger as a threat. But a second later, it launched itself straight up and over the roof of my truck and took off into the night at an astonishing speed. Laying stunned on the ground it was slow and methodical. But in the air, it was a powerful flyer.

I sat there, stunned, trying to come to terms with what I'd just seen, then continued driving at a snail's pace the rest of the way to the house. My daughter was on cloud nine, of course, and kept going on and on about fairies being real and that she'd seen one. I, on the other hand, was rambling to myself. My whole world had just been upended. I kept thinking, *Are fairies real? Is that what we just saw? If so, what else is real? Are there werewolves and mothmen and Lord-knows-what-else?*

Once we got inside, Ava went to tell her mother about our fantastic adventure, while I headed straight to my PC and started researching bats and extinct dragonflies. It was silly. The big brown bait is the largest native bat to NA, but it was a fraction of the size of what we saw, which had a wingspan of 3-4 feet. Besides, bats don't have wings like an insect, and this was no dragonfly – extinct or not.

In retrospect, I have no idea what we saw. Some have suggested that it was a young Mothman. Maybe so, but let me tell you, if that's what one looks like, they look nothing like those statues you see popping up. This entity was completely different. I suppose it could've been an extraterrestrial of some kind. Although I've never heard of one like that.

My then-agent told me what we saw was a "Brownie". Brownies are, according to her, a large species of fairy that lives high up in trees, where it shares nests with squirrels and feeds on berries and such. I don't know if I believe that, to be frank. But, as with the Mothman, if what we saw was a fairy of any species, they appear nothing like the images one traditionally sees of said creatures.

A classical image of a fairy.

Whatever it was, I'm grateful for the thing's timing. Ava had reached the age where she was starting to no longer believe in Santa Claus. Once I pointed out that fairies were obviously real, that completely changed her mind. Bought me a few more years of childhood innocence, so to speak.

That following spring, Ava and I decided to try and convince "our" fairy to come and make contact with us. We went into the nearby woods with a bowl of fresh blueberries. They were the big, juicy Costco variety – top drawer. We hiked a half mile in, found a perfectly flat tree stump that someone had cut, and sat the bowl there. We stayed there for a good 45 minutes, talking aloud so the "fairy folk" would hear us, telling them we wished to speak, that we'd brought them food, and that we meant them no harm.

I felt a little silly, although after what we'd experienced six months earlier, I had no idea what might happen. As it turned out, we got no reply. It's possible they smelled the gun oil on the .45 I had concealed beneath my shirt (cryptid behavior is an unknown quantity, but that of certain wingless, terrestrial hominids is not).

Eventually, we announced that we were leaving the food there and went on our way. The next day, Ava had school, but I promised her I would go check on our "bait".

The bowl was exactly where we'd left it, except it was empty. There was not a mark on it, no berry stain or pieces of skin, nada. It was like something had picked out the fruit piece by piece and carried it off. I know it wasn't a deer, squirrel, or racoon, as they would've made a mess and knocked the bowl around as well.

When I discussed this on an interview on *Into the Fray* radio with Shannon LeGro, I supposed that some teenager walking through the woods must've eaten the berries. She chuckled and replied, "*Right* . . . Because if *you* were walking through the woods and saw a bowl of fresh blueberries just sitting there, you'd stop and eat them?"

Shades of one of the "Shrek" movies came over me, and I realized that was pretty dumb.

Fast forward to the present, and we haven't seen the creature since. However, I have a plan to try and get evidence of one. As it gets colder, food in the woods around where we live will be in short supply. I have a fancy trail camera and a platform I plan to affix to a tree. I going to put fresh berries out as bait, but place them high enough up that deer can't reach them. This may not deter squirrels and racoons, but it's possible that, if I'm consistent, I might just get a few stills or even a quick video of one of these creatures.

I can't tell you how many times I've mentally kicked myself for not having installed the dash camera I'd purchased ages ago. If I had, said fairy would've been recorded dead to rights. It would've been brightly-lit and perfectly centered, and the footage would've gone viral for sure.

Ah well . . .

But do stay tuned. If it so happens that I manage to get some evidence before this book goes to print, you'll know. Otherwise, please make sure to follow me either on social media or via my site's monthly newsletter (www.maxhawthorne.com). Any important updates on things that go "bump in the night" will definitely be posted there.

Sketch by *Into the Fray* listener Brett Manning.

Super Predator
Identified?

It may soon be time for the mighty saltwater crocodile, *Crocodylus porosus,* to relinquish its title as the world's largest living reptile. But to what? What is this challenger, this "pretender" to the saltie's throne? Strangely enough, according to the evidence I've collected, it appears to be the species of gigantic sea turtle documented by Garry Liimatta, back in 1969. If, in fact, its existence ends up being formally documented, this creature may also prove to be the "Super Predator" – the mysterious beast that, over a decade ago, preyed on a 3-meter great white shark off Australia's infamous predator hot spot, the Bremer canyon.

A three-meter great white shark like this one became
the Super Predator's victim.

The story behind the Super Predator

The story behind the white shark known as "Alpha" being devoured by an unidentified marine predator is well-known, and was covered in detail a few years back by not one, but two hour-long documentaries: *Hunt for the Super Predator* and *The Search for the ocean's Super Predator.*

The story is shocking. Alpha was a three-meter (almost 10 feet) female great white shark that ended up being swallowed whole by an unknown carnivore. This was verified by a satellite tag attached to her, which tracked her movements. Her swim patterns were normal until, one day, she (and the tag) suddenly plummeted almost 2,000 feet into the blackness of the Bremer canyon.

A moment later, the shark's progress stopped and the temperature the tag was registering jumped from 46 degrees Fahrenheit (the temperature of the surrounding seawater) to 78 degrees (the body temperature of whatever consumed the tag and, presumably, Alpha. The temperature remained at 78 degrees while in the predator's digestive tract for the next eight days, when the tag (which showed signs of being exposed to stomach acid) was excreted and eventually washed ashore.

The identity of this mysterious shark slayer remains unconfirmed, although numerous theories have been put forward. Whatever it was, it had to be huge, fast, and capable of diving to great depths without suffering ill effects.

Based on the two aforementioned documentaries, we've been able to glean additional details about the attack. As I said, we already know that the Super Predator had an internal body temperature of 78 degrees Fahrenheit. We also know that it was capable of chasing down a 9+foot great white which could swim at 30+ mph, that it could catch and kill it in the dark, that it was an air breather (the tag's movements after the attack indicate an animal that remained at depths ranging from the surface to around 300 feet for the next eight days – behavior similar to the movements of the air-breathing killer whale), and that it had a long and slow digestive system (it took 8 days for the tag to be excreted).

If you're a subscriber to my website, or if you're one of the *Kronos Rising* series followers, you know that I explored the whole Super Predator topic back in 2017. In that blog post, I discussed why the usual suspects (a larger, cannibalistic great white, sperm and killer whales, and cephalopods) could not have been Alpha's killer. Nothing matched with them – not their movements, abilities, speed, body temperature, or digestive systems.

In short: whales are too warm, sperms too slow. Orcas can't dive that deep, larger white sharks are too cold and too slow, and cephalopods are the same temperature as the surrounding water. Not to mention, octopus and squid consume their prey in small bites with their beaks, with the latter even grinding those chunks into mush with their rasp-like tongues.

Rather than rehashing this material, I'm going to focus on a few points that have been neglected. Then we'll focus on indicators that, IMHO, suggest that the Liimatta turtle *has* to be the culprit.

One solution that was suggested is that a 16-foot white shark killed and ate Alpha. As this comparison shows, a 3-meter white shark does not fit inside a 16' shark. Granted, the larger one could kill it if it could catch it (odds are it couldn't) but even if it consumed *just* the tracker, the stomach temperature differential doesn't jibe. White sharks have a core temperature up to 25 degrees higher than the surrounding water*. The Super Predator's temp was 32 degrees higher.

* http://www.elasmo-research.org/education/topics/p_warm_body_1.htm

The abyssal Megalodon theory

First, let's discuss the "Abyssal Megalodon" theory. One of the two documentaries theorized that there might be a relict population of the extinct shark, *Otodus megalodon*, living in the ocean abysses. They supposed that one of these behemoths swam up, killed Alpha, and then returned with its victim to its home in the deep.

An entertaining tale, but the concept is a bit of a stretch. Even if a pelagic hunter like Megalodon *did* somehow adapt to live in the abyss, the facts don't support one of them rising to the surface to kill Alpha.

Most of the prevailing theories imply that Alpha was seized by the Super Predator near the surface, dragged down almost 2,000 feet into the depths, and then devoured. This is wrong. The evidence indicates that Alpha was initially attacked high up in the water column, and that she dove deep in an effort to lose her attacker.

Note: This is a documented technique that great whites use when fleeing killer whales. In the Farallon, after Orcas killed a great white, every shark in the area – a hundred animals – vanished for the rest of the season. Trackers showed at least one of them dove to 1,500 feet and swam all the way to Hawaii.[*] *If Alpha knew her enemy was an air breather, it makes sense that she would have tried the same thing in order to escape it.*

How do we know Alpha did this? By studying the satellite tracking tag's movements via a screenshot. I studied it in detail, and saw some interesting things.

---

[*] https://www.nationalgeographic.com/animals/2019/07/killer-whales-orcas-eat-great-white-sharks/

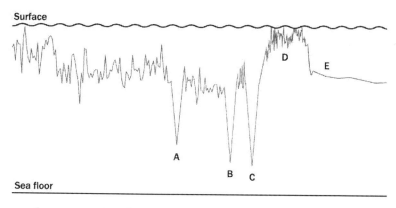

Chart recreating the extremes of Alpha's satellite tag tracking.

C: This is the tag tracking Alpha's movements right before she was eaten. At the bottom of this track, the tag's temperature suddenly jumps 32 degrees (from 46 to 78 degrees Fahrenheit). This indicates she was inside her attacker's stomach at this point.

D: This cluster of data indicates the tag's movements *after* Alpha was ingested. This period is, according to the documentary, eight days in length. During this time, the tag indicates movements ranging from the surface to around 300 feet of water. This indicates an air-breathing animal.

E: Although, to the best of my knowledge, this has not been discussed, this data cluster undoubtedly represents after the tag was excreted, and before it was retrieved. It would have drifted along the bottom, until it eventually washed ashore with the tide.

B: An additional deep dive of Alpha's. This one was made an estimated 4-6 days prior to her death and is a powerful indicator that she was attacked and pursued by something (most likely the same predator) and was able to escape it by diving deep into the abyss.

A: Yet another additional deep dive on Alpha's part. This one took place weeks prior to her death. Again, the evidence suggests the shark was attacked and pursued by something, and that she resorted to using the same instinctive technique to escape her pursuer. She escaped several of these attacks in this method, but the last time her attacker managed to either outmaneuver or outwit her and she was caught.

An unanswered question

One question that remains unanswered; why would Alpha be targeted repeatedly by the Super Predator?

Logically, this is because, as stated in one of the documentaries, she was an extremely aggressive and confident shark, hence her name "Alpha". It is likely that, if her attacker was a sea turtle, she failed to recognize it as a threat. Based on her life's experiences, and with apex predators like that being typically very few in number, she'd probably never seen one before. As a result, she could have interpreted it as being small and harmless when viewed from a distance – perhaps even potential prey. This allowed it to get close enough to make a run at her. It failed the first few times, but eventually succeeded.

A sea turtle viewed from a distance.
Could Alpha have initially assumed her attacker was small?

MONSTERS & MARINE MYSTERIES

Conclusion

The tracking data overwhelmingly indicates that shark Alpha was *not* seized and dragged to the bottom, but rather was pursued and caught nearly 2,000 feet down. Moreover, it also implies that she was *not* eaten by a Megalodon or any other predator that lives and hides out in the ocean abysses. If Alpha's killer was something that lived thousands of feet down and came up periodically to hunt (ignoring facts like speed, body temperature, and a digestive system that doesn't match), then why would it loiter around the surface for the next 8 days, acting like an air-breather?

It wouldn't have, and if it did it would have been seen. Logic dictates that it would have returned to its regular abode in the abyss, yet obviously it didn't.

No. Whatever killed Alpha encountered her high in the water column – from the tag data, I'm estimating at around the 600-foot mark – and chased her down into the deep. It didn't catch her first and then drag her down there to eat her. If it had, it would have obviously remained there. Instead, it chased her down, caught her in the dark, and consumed her there. Then, it returned to the surface (as its need for oxygen required it to) and remained there as it digested its meal.

My Theory on the Super Predator

In a previous article on my website, I stated that the evidence suggested that the Super Predator was some sort of undocumented marine reptile. We know now that, via isotope research on mosasaur and plesiosaur body temperatures, those animals are not a match. Their body temps were too hot – mammalian levels or higher. Which leads us back to the only suspect that, temperature-wise, matches – the leatherback sea turtle.

Of course, we know that leatherbacks aren't chasing and eating sharks as big or bigger than them. However, except for the size issue they have all the necessary tools for the job. They can swim at 22 mph, and a giant version that evolved to prey on large fish would be even faster. They can dive to depths of at least 4,200 feet and stay submerged for 85 minutes.[*] Even more interestingly, in the *Windfall Films* documentary, *Inside Nature's Giants: Leatherback turtle*, their digestive systems were revealed via dissection to be extremely complex – six times longer than that of other sea turtles.

If one had evolved to consume sharks, it would come as no surprise that it would take a week or more to finish the job. Lastly, leatherbacks are able to sustain a core body temperature that is substantially higher than that of the surrounding water – 32 degrees higher, in fact. And *that* is the exact temperature difference between the Super Predator's stomach and that of the surrounding sea.

Interesting, don't you think?

The leatherback sea turtle possesses almost all characteristics of the "super predator" except size.

All of this adds up to a very convincing argument. The speed, diving ability, respiration, body temperature and even digestive

---

* https://www.nationalgeographic.com/animals/reptiles/l/leatherback-sea-turtle/

system of the Super Predator all seem to indicate an animal like a leatherback sea turtle. However, leatherbacks, even at their maximum size of 1,500+ lbs. (some reports put them at over 2,000) is incapable of killing, let alone devouring a 10-foot shark that, on a rough guess, weighed six hundred pounds. Not to mention, they eat jellyfish.

But evidence *does* exist that strongly suggests there is a much larger species of sea turtle out there. A turtle similar to the leatherback in that it has no shell, but that is leaner, faster, and much, much bigger.

Obviously, I'm referring to the turtle that was seen and filmed by fisherman Garry Liimatta, back in 1969. As we previously covered, he described it as being 38' long and capable of "terrific speed". We also know that Garry's sighting is not the first of its kind; there are numerous other sightings that suggest that a turtle of this size and description exists.

Granted, these are anecdotal reports without hard evidence beyond witness testimony and drawings, but when combined with Liimatta's footage, however old and grainy it may be, it seems evident that some sort of oversized sea turtle is out there, waiting to be found. At a length of around 40 feet (the size of a gray whale), such an animal would definitely be able to chase down and consume a 3-meter great white, as easily as a big loggerhead could a two-foot-long dogfish.

If such an animal exists – one with a neck like a snake-neck turtle which, as I documented when I solved the mystery of plesiosaur's long necks, enables it to close on fish more easily by reducing the perceived pressure wave it generates[*] – and little fear of humans – it is most likely a piscivore (fish eater) or omnivore, like the loggerhead, and subsists on a diet of fish, jellyfish, and large aquatic plants. It would, based on its size, per force, give birth to live young, in the manner of extinct mosasaurs and

---

[*] https://www.kronosrising.com/
plesiosaur-necks-long-part-2-testing-theory/

pliosaurs. It probably laid soft eggs that were torn open by the hatchlings the moment they were expelled into the sea.

In terms of speed, it would be able to catch a sub-adult great white (30+ mph in bursts). It would have the ability to handle extreme pressure (as does the leatherback), be able to see in the dark with its large eyes, have a body temperature in the range of the Super Predator (32 degrees differential, again, per the leatherback) and have an extremely long and slow digestive system that could account for it taking eight days to completely digest its meal.

Possible silhouette for Liimatta's "shell-less" sea turtle based on his description.

A final thought

There is one final piece to the puzzle that may not "cinch things", but it is worth mentioning. During one of the aforementioned documentaries, it was reported that the research vessel had a sonar reading beneath them, hundreds of feet down, that matched the size of the predator they were looking for. This anomalous reading indicated a creature 35 feet long (10.5 meters long) and swimming slowly. As luck would have it, they dismissed it as a whale.

Yes, leatherbacks may exceed 20 mph when pressed, but it's common knowledge that, when moseying from place to place, they're pretty slow. So, once again, this sonar reading does seem to match the profile of a giant turtle, similar to that from the Liimatta sighting.

Put all of that together, and the evidence suggests that we may indeed have a large, unknown marine reptile roaming our oceans – something whose ancestors survived the Cretaceous extinction and grew and evolved over time. In honor of the late Garry Liimatta, who managed to garner the first footage of this elusive animal, I propose that, when concrete proof of its existence is finally gathered, it is assigned the scientific name *Titanichelys liimattii* (Liimatta's titanic turtle). I've also drafted a sketch of what I believe human visitors in a passing submarine might have seen, as the turtle in question closed on poor doomed Alpha.

Ladies and gentlemen . . . I leave it to you to decide.

Is this the SUPER PREDATOR?

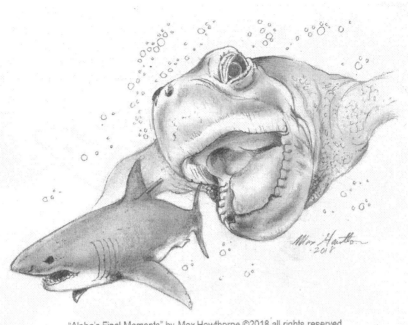

WHALE OF A SHARK?

As an author who specializes in sea monsters and does podcasts on the subject, people often reach out to me about sightings they've had (or claim to have had). Sometimes, said sightings are credible. Sometimes they're a case of exaggeration or misidentification. And sometimes, the person is flat-out lying (you know who you are). Occasionally, the tale I'm told sounds believable, yet at the same time is so patently preposterous that it's insane to even consider it.

This is one of those instances.

On August 30th of 2020 I did an extensive phone interview with a gentleman by the name of Jack Pendell. Jack is a retired Navy man, and his story dates back to the spring/summer of 1982. At that time, he was serving aboard the USS *Independence* (CV-62), an aircraft carrier commissioned in 1959. She was the fifth US warship to bear that proud name, and the final member of the *Forrestal* class of conventionally powered (non-nuclear) supercarriers. She served until she was decommissioned in 1998 and was eventually towed to Texas in 2017 to be scrapped.

Like all supercarriers, *Independence* was an enormous ship. She displaced nearly 82,000 tons at full load and was 1,070 feet in length, with a maximum beam of 270 feet and a 37-foot draft. Her ship's complement totaled over five thousand and she had a top speed of 39 mph. She was an imposing warship and, in her day, one of the mightiest on the planet.

Could there have been a living, non-human creature that posed a threat to her?

Probably not.

Could there have been a marine creature that approached her in size?

Most definitely not.

That is, unless of course, the astonishing story Jack Pendell told me is true.

The Incident

Per Jack's account, from March to June of 1982, *Independence* was on a training cruise, sailing around the Caribbean and the Gulf of Mexico. This part of the story is at least partially verifiable, as the carrier and her battle group arrived in the Mediterranean sea on June 25, 1982, to provide air support to the multinational peacekeeping force in Lebanon.[*]

Prior to *Independence*'s arrival in the Mediterranean, a then 17-to-18-year-old Jack Pendell (his birthday is April 29th) was an airman's apprentice – a "new guy". Although he was unaware of the ship's exact location (for obvious reasons, only select officers possess such knowledge), he estimates that, at the time of the incident, the carrier was northeast of the Caribbean, perhaps two hundred miles east of Puerto Rico. On a side note, he also recalls that, during their training cruise, they stopped at Fort Lauderdale, Florida during spring break.

When the sighting took place, Jack was stationed in Primary Flight Control, (Pri-Fly). He describes it as a room situated about thirty feet above the flight deck at the aft end of the island. The "island" is the command center of both the flight deck and the entire ship, and Primary Flight Control is located at the rear of it. The officer in Pri-Fly helps guide planes as they return to the ship. Per Jack: "It is surrounded by bullet proof glass on the two sides facing the flight deck, with a bubble that juts out on the corner, which is where the Air Dept. officers sit, (Air-boss & Mini-boss) to control what happens on deck. It is also about 150

* https://en.wikipedia.org/wiki/USS_Independence_(CV-62)

yards from the fantail (the rear of the carrier's flight deck), and the flight deck is 87' off the water."

The incident occurred between late April and early May in 1982. Jack was in Pri-Fly with the Air-boss. It was in between flight operations and they were watching as people on the hangar deck (below them, and therefore out of sight) started dumping trash overboard (apparently, standard operating procedure). This "trash" included quantities of garbage from the mess hall (chicken bones, scraps, etc.). For the men stationed in Pri-Fly, one of the ways they passed the time was to keep an eye on the fantail and wait to see what would come up and "snag a bag". I would imagine carriers like *Independence* have a perpetual escort of hungry fish, including an array of sharks, that follow them, waiting for an easy meal.

It was lunchtime at this point, and Jack and the Air-boss were the only ones on duty. As they watched the feeding frenzy building in the ship's wake, all of a sudden, an enormous, brown whale shark's fin rose up out of the water, directly behind the carrier. Jack was amazed at the size of the fin which, from his position, appeared to be every bit as wide as the aft end of the flight deck (he estimated the fantail to be 130' - 150' wide, official measurements put it at 148 feet).

Let me repeat that, and please try not to laugh. The *base* of the dorsal fin – meaning its widest point where it met the shark's body – was as wide as the aft end of the flight deck from where Jack and the Air-boss stood. In terms of their location, they were 117 feet above the surface of the water (the carrier's deck height of 87 feet plus the island's 30-foot height) and they estimated the fin was around 250+/- yards from their location. That put it less than one boat length behind *Independence*'s stern (and her props).

Jack couldn't say for sure how big the entire animal was, but by comparing the width of the dorsal fin they saw to that of an average whale shark, he estimated it was an impossible *nine hundred feet in length!*

No, that is not a typo.

He said he remembered the fin covering the entire width of the wake directly behind the carrier. He also stated that they watched it as it cut across their wake from left to right and continued on toward the horizon. It held its course until it reached what he figured was the halfway point between them and the horizon, which he estimated as being nine miles away, at which point it submerged.

I did some calculating, and at a height of 117, feet Jack and his superior could actually see 13.3 miles. Half of that would be around 6.6 miles. Also, objects compress visually as they move toward the horizon, and what appears to be the halfway point is technically not. Regardless, the two men watched the fin for some time before it disappeared. He also told me that, right before it submerged, the Air-Boss turned to him and asked, "Did you *see* that?" to which he pointed at it and, shaking his head, sputtered, "Uh-huh!"

If it was real, how big was the shark?

Now that you've had a moment to chortle and/or scoff, before I get into trying to extrapolate the mind-blowing size of the shark that was "spotted" (whale shark pun intended), let me clear the air on two things. The first is that, when interviewing Jack, I asked him flat-out if he and the Air-boss had been drinking or had engaged in the use of "recreational pharmaceuticals". He stated quite vehemently that they were both stone sober. With them both responsible for an array of very expensive planes landing safely on the deck, not to mention their pilots, I'm inclined to believe him.

The second is that there is no way that Jack was trying to pull a hoax on me. I know this because I found out about his encounter via Simon J. Pierce, a marine biologist I know. Simon happens to be the world's foremost expert on whale sharks.

When Jack first saw the shark behind *Independence,* he was a kid. He knew it was a whale shark based on footage he'd seen and the color and spots. He told me his initial thought was, *"Man, that's a big whale shark!"* But he assumed they simply got that big. It wasn't until many years later that he realized every shark he saw on television was small compared to just the *dorsal* of what he'd seen.

Eventually, Jack reached out to Simon and relayed his experience. This was back in 2015. I only became acquainted with Simon in 2018, when I sought him out for help identifying a beached carcass, so any correlation is impossible.

With that said, and giving Jack's tale the benefit of the doubt (yes, it's quite a "stretch", pun intended), let's try to do some number crunching and see if the fish was anywhere near as big as he thought.

The first thing we're going to do is go over the layout of a supercarrier like *Independence.* Based on the diagram below, you can see the location of Primary Flight Control (A) where Jack and his commanding officer were stationed. And (B) the carrier's fantail which, as we know, measured 148 feet in width. It is from beneath this fantail, in the hangar bay, that seamen tossed bags of garbage into the sea, creating a chum line that may have attracted a lot more than they anticipated.

I estimate that location A (Pri-Fly) is around 400 feet from the fantail. According to Jack, the dorsal fin was around 250 yards (750 feet) behind the ship when it broke the surface, and the fin's maximum width at the base matched the width of the wake behind the carrier.

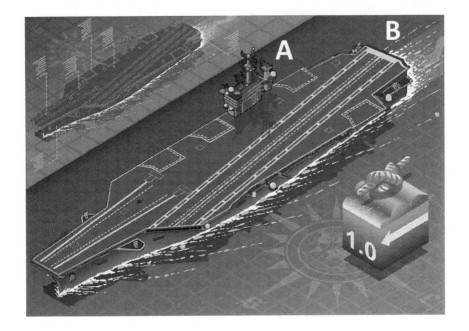

The next question is: how wide was the wake?

Jack estimated the carrier's speed around the time of the sighting at around 20 knots, which equates to about 23 mph. That's a far cry from the ship's maximum speed of 39 mph, which would, perforce, result in a significantly wider wake. Interestingly, 20 knots is similar to the cruising speed of large ocean liners, so the number makes sense.

I've studied assorted images of carriers underway, and *Independence* in particular. From the available evidence, the wake behind the ship while moving at normal cruising speed tends to be similar in diameter to the fantail or a bit larger. At higher speeds it increases dramatically.

This next image shows *Independence* maneuvering at what appears to be slow cruising speed. The wake behind the ship appears almost like a slick on the surface, and is similar in width to the ship's fantail.

USS Independence (CV-62) at sea.
Image courtesy of the National Archives (public domain)

This next image is the stern of *Independence* as she moves at what appears to be cruising speed. The wake is now at least as wide as the fantail – probably more so, especially as it spreads out behind the ship. Also, of interest in this particular shot is the hangar bay below decks. This is the spot from which garbage was tossed out.

Stern view of USS Independence (CV-62). Image courtesy National Archives (public domain)

Lastly, we have a shot of an F-18 Hornet maneuvering toward an unidentified carrier. The carrier is obviously moving at an accelerated rate – possibly performing evasive maneuvers. The wake behind the ship is enormous. I estimate it to be wider than the flight deck's maximum beam which, going by the *Forrestal* class's deck diagram is approximately 310 feet.*

For purposes of our calculations, and in the interest of being conservative (not that it matters much when trying to calculate the size of a fish that, purportedly, was as big as a kaiju) we're going to assume that the ship was, as Jack stated, moving at standard cruising speed. This gives us a wake approximately the width of the ship's fantail, or around 150 feet.

---

* https://upload.wikimedia.org/wikipedia/commons/c/c5/Forrestalclass_aircraft_carrier_deck_plan_1962.png

Before I do my usual number-crunching, and in the interest of complete disclosure, I'd like to add one minor detail. Jack's account states that the dorsal fin was as wide as the carrier's wake. But it also states that the fin looked like it was the same width as their 148-foot-wide fantail, when seen from 400 feet away. Their distance from the fantail doesn't matter as much as the distance of the fin *from* the fantail.

If the fin was, as stated, 750 feet behind the ship when it broke the surface, and was still the width of the fantail, we are looking at what is known as forced perspective. Forced perspective is an optical illusion that makes objects appear larger or smaller when viewed in front of or behind other objects. For example, if I have a three-pound bass in my hand and I extend it out toward the camera, it suddenly looks like it weighs twelve pounds or more because, as it moves further away from me it moves closer to the lens. It appears to grow and I appear to shrink.

In the case of the dorsal fin surfacing behind *Independence*, if it was 750 feet away (which is one football field less than one boat length, as the carrier was 1070 feet long) but still matched the fantail in terms of size, then it was actually wider than the fantail, which is, once again, 148 feet across. How wide is hard to say, but I would estimate that it would probably appear to be one third smaller than it actually was if it was right on top of you.

If Jack's statement that the fin was as wide as the fantail is accurate, then it was wider than 150 feet across its base. It also implies that the wake behind the boat was wider than the fantail, especially 750 feet back, where it would have spread out a bit, perhaps a full 200 feet across.

Obviously, we're getting more and more into a place where we don't want to be. A place where low-budget sci-fi films are cranked out and sharks the size of ocean liners prowl our oceans. That said, since I've already dived into the rabbit hole, I may as well keep on falling.

If (and the following are all mighty big "ifs") Jack and his commanding officer actually saw what he says they did (both he and I have attempted to contact his commanding officer in the hopes of getting corroboration), and *if* the fin they saw was indeed a whale shark, and *if* it was as wide as the wake behind the boat, and *if* that wake was *only* 150 feet, then this is what we're looking at:

Based on known whale shark proportions, and with a dorsal fin with a basal width of 150 feet (dorsal fin diameter to length is usually in the 1:7 or 1:6.9 ratio range) we'd be looking at a fish that measured between 1,035 and 1050 feet in length. The dorsal would be 85-90 feet high, and the caudal fin (tail) would tower around 260 feet from lobe tip to lobe tip. The animal's head would be around 130 feet across, with a mouth over 100 feet wide.

Just to put that in perspective, a gigantic blue whale or a herd of elephants would fit in the shark's mouth with no problem.

On the other hand, *if* (again, we're <u>really</u> iffy about all this), Jack was correct about the dorsal being as wide as the fantail. And *if* my calculations in terms of forced perspective are roughly accurate (meaning, perforce, that the wake and hence, the dorsal, would have been wider than the fantail if it was directly alongside) and it was one-third larger, i.e. 200 hundred feet at the base, the number would be even scarier.

Then, we'd be looking at a fish that was an unimaginable *1,400 feet in length*. It would have a tail nearly 350 feet high and a dorsal that soared as much as 120 feet into the sky. Its head would be 175 feet across.

Then there's the craziest question; how much would it weigh?

I can smell the derision now. But, remember, I'm just the messenger.

Based on an average whale shark being 32 feet long and weighing 10 tons (per Wikipedia), a specimen 1,050 feet in length would tip the scales at around 352,875 tons. It would weigh more than four times the weight of *Independence,* and be the largest living thing in the history of the planet.

Oh, and if it was 1,400 feet long? How does 837,402 tons sound?

Ridiculous?

Yeah, I'm thinking the same thing.

But, hey. For those of us that believe marine cryptids exist, one can always hope.

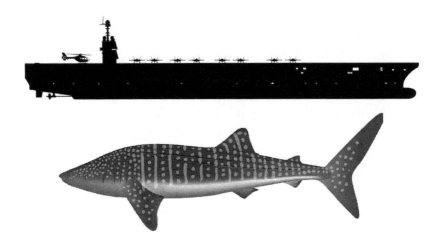

A "conservative" comparison of an impossibly large (900')
whale shark to an aircraft carrier.

Is it physically possible?

Obviously, the possibility of a fish growing larger than "Godzilla" is tough to wrap one's head around. It defies the laws of both physics and nature, at least as we know them. But is it in any way possible? Can a whale shark get that big? Or *any* animal for that matter?

It's a known fact that some marine animals are able to grow to prodigious sizes, at least in part because of the water's supporting embrace. The Megalodon shark reached 50 feet and 40 tons. And the blue whale can reach double that length and weigh nearly five times as much. There have been sightings of squid that stretched 175 feet, and jellyfish of impossible proportions.

So, could a whale shark grow to that size?

Whale sharks are known to reach a maximum size of around 20 meters, or a bit over sixty feet. For an animal to reach the freakish proportions of the animal that surfaced behind *Independence*, it would have to be more than just an outsized individual.

Much more.

It would have to be a mutant of some kind.

Sharks have skeletons of cartilage. That imposes limits on them, especially in terms of speed and maneuverability. It is true that calcification does occur at times in large sharks, particularly in the jaw regions of adult great whites. The cartilage becomes harder and stronger. Not true bone, per se, but sturdier than normal. Could that help to explain a whale shark getting that big?

Perhaps. But whale sharks aren't predators. They're plankton feeders that graze like cows, so strong jaws are irrelevant. They don't have to chase their food, so speed wouldn't be a factor, which could be advantageous at extreme sizes. Although small and medium-sized whale sharks are sometimes preyed upon by great whites and Orcas, a sixty-footer would be relatively immune to attack. And a monster the size of the one that Jack reported would have no natural enemies. The only threat to it, beside old age, would be a ship strike. And even then, it would take an immense vessel to cause it harm.

Although sharks are indeterminate growers – meaning they grow their entire lives – I find the possibility of a whale shark reaching half a kilometer hard to believe, at least under normal circumstances. They're not immortal, and upon maturing their growth slows. It would take millennia for a whale shark to reach such proportions.

The only plausible explanation that I can come up with – and I'll tell you now, it's an insane thought – is that the fish's DNA was somehow altered.

Based on the research I did for this book, the only thing that comes to mind is one I touched on when researching South Side Sea Monster. During my discussions with Rodney Ross, the sole surviving witness of said cryptid, I showed him a photo of the one creature that I thought sounded vaguely like what he saw – a Goosefish. He said the mouth looked very similar, and the fish he saw was broad and flat like that with no dorsal fin. But he also said what he saw looked "deformed". So, could something have happened to a fish that normally maxes out at five feet, to turn it into a sixty-foot behemoth with jaws fifteen feet across?

Coincidentally, in 1967, nine years before Rodney Ross and his father were attacked by said creature, a UFO crashed into nearby Shag Harbour*. Fishermen and the Coast Guard, while searching for survivors of what they initially believed to be a passenger plane crash, reported a thick yellow foam floating on the water around the crash site. Could this foam have had prop-erties that, in less than a decade, turned a Goosefish fry into a whale-sized monster?

Nasa recently admitted that UFOs are real. So, anything is possible. And if that *is* a possibility, with said foam drifting with the tide and affecting plankton, krill, and all matter of marine life, could a young whale shark have consumed some of this affected/infected life and had its cells altered to the point that it experienced a form of gigantism that caused it to grow at a geometric rate?

The notion is astonishing, I know. But given the impossible size of the shark Jack reported – which, by the way, was six years after Rodney Ross's sighting – it's the only thing I can think of.

Improbable? Of course. But in the words of Sir Arthur Conan Doyle's Sherlock Holmes, "When you have eliminated the impossible, whatever remains, however improbable, must be the truth".

---

* https://en.wikipedia.org/wiki/Shag_Harbour_UFO_incident

USS *Independence* (CV-62) with superimposed image of a whale shark's dorsal based on the witness's description. Image courtesy the National Archives (public domain)

What could it eat?

If a whale shark the size of the Empire State building actually existed, what would it eat? What *could* it eat?

The short answer is anything it wanted, provided it could catch it.

Such an animal would be beyond ponderous, probably swimming at the same speed a normal sized whale shark does, around three mph. But being planktivorous, it wouldn't have to be fast. Schools of krill, for example, average over 100 yards in length and move with the tide. They are easy to catch.

Technically, with a mouth over 100 feet across, it could inhale entire shoals of fish and squid as well, plus larger fish when opportunity permitted, and even pods of dolphins (although I daresay the latter would be speedy and smart enough to see it coming and get out of Dodge). Moreover, if the story is true, it probably surfaced behind *Independence* to swallow all the sharks and fish that were feeding on the garbage thrown into the sea, as well as the garbage itself.

So, yes. Between plankton and schools of fish, there would be plenty of food for such a creature to feed on. At least, one of them.

Of course, said animal would not be immortal. And being unable to mate, it would eventually die of old age and sink to the bottom. If it was real, most likely it's dead already; one more marine mystery, lost to the annals of time.

If it wasn't a shark, what else could it have been?

I don't believe that Jack made up his story. I believe he saw *something.*

I know that he wrote to the navy about what he'd seen and was ignored. And I know that his attempt to contact the marine biologist I mentioned availed him naught. He doesn't seem like an attention seeker. In fact, he didn't even reach out to me. I heard about his story from Simon and I reached out to *him.*

That said, assuming Jack's tale is true, is it possible that it was a case of mistaken identity? Could he have seen something else that he took to be an enormous whale shark?

Given that the dorsal fin Jack saw rose up in the carrier's wake and then traveled for miles while at least two men watched it (note: if any of the flight crew or members of the garbage disposal details on *Independence* in 1982 saw this animal, please reach out to me), the notion of a sunken ship somehow popping to the surface seems highly unlikely. The only other possibility I can come up with would be some sort of submarine.

The Soviet's had their vaunted *Typhoon*-class nuclear boats functioning as early as 1981. They are monsters – 574 feet long, 75+ feet wide, and displace 48,000 tons submerged. Could a *Typhoon* have been outfitted with some sort of realistic "dorsal fin" to cover its conning tower so as to allow it to surface around American warships?

The idea is almost as ludicrous as a 1,400-foot shark. A dorsal fin attachment 150-200 feet wide would be enormous, even for a submarine that size. And the strain it would put on the vessel would be tremendous. Not to mention, the loss of speed and reduced ability to submerge and hide from attackers. And then there's the noise factor, increased sonar signature, etc. . . .

I suppose it's just as likely as a whale shark that got as big or bigger than an aircraft carrier. But I tend to think Soviet engineers were smarter than that. Who knows? Whale sharks are listed as living up to 130 years. If its lifespan wasn't cut short by its accelerated growth or a ship strike (or a military one), maybe Jack's giant is still out there somewhere.

Personally, I like the notion of anchoring up next to an island, only to discover it's a real-life *Leviathan*. I just hope the boat I'm on isn't named *Jonah*.

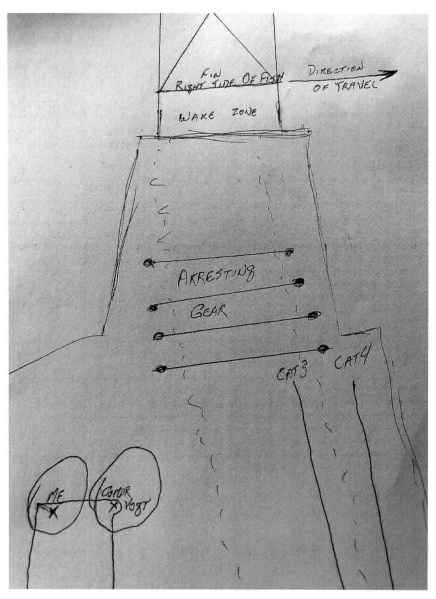

Sketch of *Independence*'s sighting (deck, wake and fin)
drawing by Jack Pendell.

Possible Mosasaur Attack on Orca?

On November 30th of 2018, the Facebook page known as *Carcharodon Carcharias* released a video of a pair of killer whales swimming off the coast of Norway. They were moving slowly through a sea of detritus (upon further research, more likely a cloud of fish scales). The smaller female was the focal point of the video and was followed by a large male which swam below her, keeping her company and, presumably, also guarding her.

I was immediately struck by how badly wounded the female was. Her body was literally riddled with nasty puncture marks and she was missing a good portion of her right pectoral fin. It had been savaged, then torn clean off. You could also tell that she was extremely malnourished. She was sporting what is known as a "peanut head" – a term marine biologists use to describe the loss of cranial mass in an emaciated Orca.

Although I had previously received permission from the aforementioned page to use the video for analysis, they are apparently defunct now. As such, even under fair use I cannot publish stills here; but the video clips and my analysis of same are still available on my YouTube channel. I encourage you to visit. It is quite compelling.

As a substitute, I have provided diagrams that, although crude, attempt to shed light on what may be astonishing evidence. The bite marks on the Orca are very unusual. In fact, I sent stills to marine biologist *par excellence* Simon J. Pierce –

someone who swims with whales, whale sharks, and worse – and asked what he thought of them. He replied:

"In the absence of much of a clue, I'd suspect that another orca was (badly) bullying it. Interspecific aggression is common enough in dolphins. I've never seen pictures of wounds like this though."

I found it interesting that the wounds didn't stand out as killer whale bites to Simon. I will attempt to analyze the bite marks momentarily, but to be fair, there is only one documented instance of a wild Orca attacking and killing another. It was a case of infanticide, and took place in March of 2018 off Vancouver Island.* During this incident, an adult bull killer whale attacked and killed a day-old calf, while his mother prevented the calf's mother from intervening. The male seized the baby by the flukes and held it underwater until it drowned.

There was no feeding, hence cannibalism was ruled out, and it was believed by the researchers observing the behavior that it was an attempt to enable the bull to mate with the mother, once its calf was dead. This is similar to invading male lions wiping out nursing cubs after taking over a pride. With the cubs gone the lionesses soon go into estrus, enabling the males to mate and pass on their genes.

Of course, Orcas are far more intelligent and family-oriented than big cats. So, this was, indeed, a rare and unusual occurrence.

That said, let's take a look at the wounds sustained by this cow Orca and see where that leads. The following diagram shows the extensive damage the young female suffered. According to the video, her assigned name was *Scratchii*, and she is a calf.

---

* https://www.nationalgeographic.com/news/2018/03/orca-killer-whale-infanticide-calf-video-canada-spd/

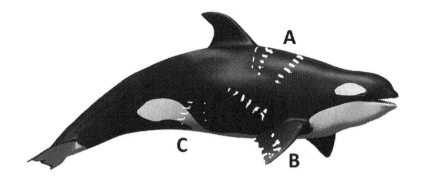

There are three definite bite marks present on Scratchii's right side (note: we have no images of the left side of her body and do not know if there were additional wounds). The first (**A**) is indicated by a large pattern of punctures that are present on her upper back, right in front of the dorsal fin. The second (**B**) is located on her chest region and appears to have enveloped her right pectoral fin as well. And the third (**C**) is on her lower abdomen, right where the white patch extends up from her belly.

Clearing the air

Before I do get into bite shapes, measurements, etc., let me just state that these markings were definitely the result of aggression from another organism – most likely an attempt at predation. They were not caused by a boat prop or net. You can Google images by the hundreds and see that. So, let's get that out of the picture immediately.

Bite breakdowns/measurements

Unfortunately, I have been unable to recontact the filmmakers, so an analysis of Scratchii in terms of age and size is nigh impossible. However, we will work with the facts as we know them and, in the interest of science, be as conservative as possible in our calculations.

The first thing to consider are the Orcas that reside off Norway. According to an interview with naturalist and marine videographer Patrick Dykstra, who runs *Natural World Safaris'* Orca-watching trips, the adult whales range from 23 to 32 feet in length.* That would make them among the largest of killer whales, and suggests that they are resident Type-2 Eastern North Atlantic Orcas that prey on fish and marine mammals (mainly seals and cetaceans) and reside in coastal regions. There are also pods of Type-1 Eastern North Atlantic Orcas that migrate through there as well. These whales are slightly smaller and tend to follow schools of fish – in this case, herring (Note: they have been known to take seals as well). Again, lack of evidence prevents me from being exacting, but as the video was released in November, and the herring spawn along the coast of Norway from February to March, I am inclined to believe the Orcas in the video are, indeed, Type-2s.

Based on the shape of her fin, we know that Scratchii is a female. According to Wikipedia, an adult female 23 feet in length (apparently, the lower range provided for the Norway pods) would weigh 4.4 tons.**

However, we also know that Scratchii is not an adult. The problem then is, without knowing her age, it is difficult to give any kind of size estimate for her. According to SeaWorld*** Orca calves are 8.5 feet at birth. They gain 25 inches their first year and 21 inches their second. Based on Scratchii's physique (flipper and head size, peduncle thickness, etc.), it appears to me that she is several years old, most likely post-weaned. So, if we go with the most conservative estimate and say she is only two years old, that would make her around 13 feet in length. Going by the size of the bull Orca that follows her, deeper down, it is

* https://www.travelandleisure.com/trip-ideas/nature-travel/dive-with-orcas-norway-natural-world-safaris

** https://en.wikipedia.org/wiki/Killer_whale

*** https://seaworld.org/animals/all-about/killer-whale/care-of-young/

likely she is larger than that. But at this point, and with no other evidence available, we'll have to settle for those numbers.

Using a frame from the original footage, the width of the bite mark on Scratchii's dorsal region **A** is approximately one-sixth of her length. If she is ~13' long, that suggests a mid-jaw bite diameter of around two feet. The length of the bite is hard to calculate, as the attacker's jaws fastened onto the whale's dorsal region, but they must have been both long and capable of a tremendous gape. The portion that is present is longer than the bite is wide while viewed laterally. Judging by the tear marks that are evident around the tooth punctures, it is evident that the attacker was able to fasten its jaws onto the Orca's back and shake it back and forth. It was a vicious assault, intended to incapacitate or kill it.

It is also evident that the attacker's teeth slipped at one point during the attack, as there is a second, albeit shallower, set of tooth punctures to the left of the dorsal bite. This suggests that predator's fangs were not deeply embedded and tore free, presumably as the young whale fought to free itself. In the original footage you can see how the teeth sliced back toward the attacker's throat as they slipped, supporting this.

If I had to guess, I would estimate that the attacking creature's jaws were somewhat narrow and wedge-shaped, lengthwise, probably somewhere in the realm of five feet. Keep in mind, this is conservative spit-balling as we have no definitive facts in terms of the calf's measurements. Even so, it is apparent that we're looking at a large predator.

Whereas bite **A** was launched at Scratchii from above, bite **B** appears to have come at her from below. The attacker seized the calf by the chest region – avoiding her jaws and making it impossible to fight back – and bit down. It may have been seeking to crush the whale's rib cage or suffocate it. The attacker's jaws were long enough to pincer the whale's chest and envelope its right pectoral fin in the process. It must have been a struggle to do so, however, as we only see one set of torn tooth marks on the whale's flank and fin. The raggedness of the marks suggests that, again, the young Orca was able to break free (perhaps with help).

Additionally, and as the punctures on the pectoral fin bear out, as the attacker's jaws slipped, they fastened onto the right pectoral fin. The attacker then held on like a pit bull. The fin quickly gave out, and was either bitten through or torn off during the protracted struggle.

I suspect that bite **C** was the final strike. I base this on the fact that the attacker was unable to get a good grip and its teeth slipped out leaving thin grooves that run like paint streaks toward the whale's flukes. This implies that the teeth weren't fully embedded and the Orca managed to rip free from its attacker.

Recreation of "Scratchii" with her unseen mother.
Note the calf's assorted wounds.

What was it?

In the interest of leaving no stone (or coral reef) unturned, I'm going to consider all the "usual suspects" as I attempt to deduce what manner of organism initiated this attack. There is an assortment of potential candidates, including the aforementioned bull Orca, a large shark, the saltwater crocodile, a sperm whale, false killer whale or giant squid.

I share Simon's opinion when he stated he'd never seen wounds like that. To me they do not look like the bite patterns typically inflicted by killer whales. Their teeth are closer together than those of whatever mauled Scratchii. Additionally, the bites are very large – even considering she's a calf – and as I said would've required a tremendous gape in order to wrap around her body like they did. Orca's are very "beefy". Lastly, there is the matter of bite width. I did some ventral/palatal measuring of Orca skull images courtesy of the Royal BC Museum. The maxilla's maximum width is around a 1:3.3 ratio when compared to overall skull length. If Scratchii's attacker had a mid-jaw bite diameter of two feet, that means that, if it was an Orca, the skull would've been 6.6 feet in length. That would suggest a killer whale some fifty feet in length – obviously impossible.

A shark is definitely out. Discounting the fact that attacking a member of an Orca pod would be tantamount to suicide (think of a coyote attacking a member of a wolf pack) the bites of white, mako and tiger sharks are very distinctive and tend to be round or oval-shaped. Whatever attacked the young cow had a triangular bite pattern similar to that of an enormous crocodile.

And speaking of crocodiles, we can cross one of them off the list as well. The largest crocodile ever documented, a saltie named *Lolong*, measured 20 feet 3 inches in length, with a skull 27.5 inches in length (700 mm). It would take a much larger animal to gain a grip on the barrel-shaped dorsal region of even a young Orca, and bite **B** suggests an attacker with a skull far longer than Lolong's. In fact, the bite *width* is almost as big as Lolong's skull was *long*. Additionally, no crocodile we know of could survive in the frigid waters around Norway, let alone be so brazen as to go after a member of a killer whale pod.

I do not believe a sperm whale was responsible. Besides the fact that a sperm whale would have no reason to attack an Orca calf, bite marks from a *Physeter macrocephalus* look very different. A sperm whale's jaw is comparatively narrow (thinner than bite **A** on Scratchii) and the two rows of teeth run parallel to one another, as opposed to the obviously wedge-shaped bite mark that tops the cow Orca's dorsal region. In addition, the teeth of a sperm whale are more widely-spaced and blunter, eliminating it as a potential candidate.

Note: during my analysis of the footage I zoomed in on a still of Scratchii from below – a difficult prospect, as the image is small and grainy – to examine bite mark **C***. There seems to be a faint indication of damage to the opposite side of the body that matches the tooth punctures on the right rear flank. This suggests that the attacker possessed both mandibular and maxillary teeth. Cachalots (sperm whales) only possess teeth in their lower jaws, again eliminating one of them as a candidate.*

A false killer whale isn't even worth mentioning, but in the interest of completeness I've included it. They're too small, their jaws aren't big enough, and some species of Orca prey on them.

That leaves a species of cephalopod. Again, we're talking about a predator with a large, wedge-shaped head lined with teeth, not a beak. The bite marks are 100% not a match, and killer whales also eat giant squid.

Anything else, including a "Megalodon strike" is so far removed from reality that it's not worth addressing. In fact, the more I look at the bite marks the more I get the impression that – as astonishing as it seems – they were the result of an attack from some sort of marine reptile. Put another way, a species of sea crocodile or mosasaur appears to be the only plausible explanation.

But is that possible?

Well, to once again utilize a line from Sir Arthur Conan Doyle's immortal Sherlock Holmes: *"When you have eliminated the impossible, whatever remains, however improbable, must be the truth."*

With that in mind, I decided to do some makeshift forensics. I took an image of a mosasaur jaw, put it in the approximate size range, and compared it to the bite marks on the killer whale's right flank. For the record, it was the cranium of the genus *Prognathodon*, a macropredatory mosasaur confirmed to have reached forty feet in length (Note: I have a fossil in my collection that suggests they reached seventy). The teeth matched perfectly in terms of placement. The only ones that didn't were missing from the original fossil, and if I went by the empty sockets, those matched as well.

Does that then prove that a relict population of mosasaur – or some similar creature – still exists? Definitely not, but it does make for an intriguing argument.

After all, *something* attacked poor Scratchii.

Unanswered questions

Scratchii was not a newborn, so attempted infanticide was not an option. And why kill a young cow that was already weaned and was an established member of the pod? That makes no sense. Also, there is a large bull shadowing her – possibly her father – and presumably on guard duty. Additionally, the calf's wounds suggest either a tenacious attacker that came at her repeatedly, or multiple attackers with murderous intent. Either way, when you couple that with the obvious bite shape and size discrepancies, I believe it is incredibly unlikely that another killer whale did the damage we see on this calf.

I would point out two other things of note. First, Scratchii looks emaciated. She could be sick from an infection from the bites she received (some reptiles like monitor lizards have highly infectious, even venomous bites) or so badly injured that she is unable to eat. Based on the scarring and her condition, the attack most likely took place weeks earlier, yet she still appears to be suffering from it.

Second, where is Scratchii's mother? Orca moms are incredibly protective and devoted. Reference the one that carried her dead infant's body around for *seventeen days* after it died.* Granted, the Norway footage is a very short clip, but we do see that big bull keeping her company. Why is her mother not there? Is she simply off camera or did something happen to her? Might she have perished protecting her child?

Graphic artwork reconstruction of a pod of *Orcinus orca*.

What might have happened?

Trying to decipher out how the attack on Scratchii took place is almost as hard as figuring out what did it. I'm fairly confident

---

* https://www.nationalgeographic.com/animals/2018/08/orca-mourning-calf-killer-whale-northwest-news/

that none of the usual suspects were responsible. But what did all that damage is anyone's guess. And when I say damage I'm not kidding. Biting off half a pectoral fin isn't bullying. That's like you or I losing a hand. If I had to go out on a limb (with a chain saw) I might suggest that we start to take extant mosasaur sightings a bit more seriously. Anecdotal reports are one thing. But a killer whale swimming around with horrific bite marks on it is something else altogether.

Think about it. In my opinion, we more or less *know* that Garry Liimatta saw and filmed a sea turtle the size of a bus. If it's out there, why not a species of marine monitor lizard that supposedly died out alongside the non-avian dinosaurs?

All suppositions aside, if I look at Scratchii's injuries as a tactician, I can make a pretty good guess as to what went down.

The dorsal bite **A** (shown below) was probably the first strike. I believe there were two attackers. (There have been multiple reports of mosasaur-like creatures hunting in pairs) It is possible that the first one hit the young Orca from above, attempting to immobilize her and break her back/neck. That failing, it would have most likely attempted to drown her.

The second attack **B** was from an animal that rushed up and seized Scratchii by the chest. This was probably an additional attempt to finish her off, either by crushing her ribs or forcing out her air. Once she drowned her distraught pod-mates would eventually abandon her body, allowing her attackers to feed with impunity.

The latter reinforces my belief that there were multiple assailants. Orcas are the ocean's apex predators. They live in family units and will certainly kill to protect their own. Anything targeting a calf would have to come in at high speed and do as much damage as possible before they were driven off. It is likely that was the plan – strike, inflict terminal damage, and then retreat and play the waiting game. A similar tactic is used by white sharks after they initiate a "bite and spit" ambush on a large and formidable elephant seal.

How the dorsal bite on the Orca calf might look when seen from above.

The last bite, **C**, was probably inflicted by the same animal that seized Scratchii by the abdomen. Once its grip slipped and it was left with nothing but a piece of pectoral fin in its mouth, the attacker probably tried to reacquire its grip on the desperately flailing calf. It managed to inflict a grazing strike on the young Orca's vent region as it sought to flee, but was unable to secure a full lock-on bite. As a result, the young whale managed to escape (or was rescued by members of its pod).

I have tried to track down information on Scratchii. It's very odd. Not only is the group gone from Facebook, I can't find any record of her on Google either. It's like she never existed. If anyone has any additional information about this whale, please reach out to me at www.maxhawthorne.com/

In summation, does all this confirm that there is a population of "extinct" marine crocodiles or Mosasaurs still roaming our oceans? Who can say? Is there another explanation for the Orca's assorted wounds and condition – one that I haven't thought of?

I don't know. What do you think?

Under cover of darkness, a mosasaur attacks an Orca calf.
Could this have happened?

OCTOPUS GIGANTEUS?

For those familiar with the "St. Augustine Monster" – an enormous mass of rotting tissue that washed ashore near St. Augustine, Florida in 1896 – you probably know it was initially believed to be the carcass of a gigantic octopus. It was even assigned the binomial nomenclature, *Octopus giganteus,* meaning, "giant octopus".

In terms of confirmation from the scientific community, however, the carcass went back and forth for the next one hundred years. It was written off as a globster (a free-floating mass of whale blubber, shed from the carcass of a dead cetacean as its body decays), then relisted as a giant squid, then declared a hoax, and then a cephalopod again. I remember reading in the *Guinness Book of World Records,* decades ago, that, based on tissue analysis, it was "confirmed" to be a monstrous octopus with a tentacular span of two hundred feet. Finally, in 1994, formal cellular testing and DNA analysis was done on tissue samples preserved from the original carcass, and it was proven to be whale blubber.

So much for the St. Augustine "Monster", and so much for proof of a giant octopus. At least for that particular one. But *are* there enormous octopi, roaming the ocean's depths and posing a threat to everything around them?

A giant Pacific octopus. Does a gargantuan version
of this animal prowl our oceans?

In my bestselling *Kronos Rising: Kraken* trilogy I decided to introduce a new marine "monster" to vie with the *Kronosaurus imperators* I'd created for the series. In came the Kraken (or "Krake" – plural) in the form of a mated pair of monstrous octopuses.

For the sake of realism, I bestowed my mammoth mollusks with a plausible backstory. I made them a long-lived species that inhabited the ocean's extreme abysses. They were a product of bathymetric gigantism, AKA deep sea gigantism, where extreme cold results in both larger cell sizes and longer lifespans in indeterminate growers. I made my Krake highly carnivorous: super predators that lurked in submarine canyons, waiting for sperm whales to descend as they hunted squid, and feeding on them. I even traced their lineage back to the "Triassic Kraken", and topped it all off by giving them suckers that exuded powerful enzymes (molecular acid) to make them even more lethal.

Not something you'd want to encounter while snorkeling.

Fiction aside, sightings of gigantic squid and octopi go back centuries. In the Caribbean they're called *Lusca*, and are reported to inhabit (among other places) the blue holes off Andros Island, in the Bahamas. There, the cephalopods supposedly range from seventy-five to as much as two hundred feet in length.[*]

In Japan, there have been multiple sightings of a gigantic, red-skinned octopus-like beast with monstrous eyes and tentacles called the *Akkorokamui*. It is believed to inhabit Funka Bay in Hokkaido and, according to legend, reaches an incredible size, with some estimates as high as 120 meters (almost 400 feet).

That sounds like quite a *stretch* (pun intended), but there are credible (and more realistic) reports from Hawaii of sizable octopuses. Specimens with tentacular spans of up to fifty feet have reportedly been killed, and there was one 1950 report by a Madison Rigdon of an octopus with a body "the size of a car" being attacked by sharks off Oahu. It defended itself with arms 30 feet in length, lined with suckers the size of dinner plates. Also in 1950, a fisherman named Val Ako was reef diving for sea turtles, when he spotted an octopus with a reported tentacular span of 75 feet.[**]

2014 Sanibel sighting: Was it a real *Octopus giganteus*?

A few years back, I was speaking with a reader who, as it turned out, had an encounter with an enormous cephalopod that he believes was an octopus. When he first relayed his experience to me, Demetrius (a pseudonym, for privacy's sake) thought what he saw was perfectly normal. He believed that octopi regularly reached the size of the creature he and his friends faced.

[*] https://en.wikipedia.org/wiki/Lusca

[**] https://www.mauisaltandsage.com/single-post/2018/04/03/Article-Part-2-The-Bizarre-Mystery-Monsters-of-Hawaii

They do not. And I cleared that up lickety-split.

To set the stage, Demetrius's encounter took place in 2014, off the coast of Sanibel Island, Florida. Sanibel is both an island and a city. It is also a popular tourist destination, due to its shell beaches and an assortment of wildlife, including bald eagles, alligators, manatees, and even a crocodile of late. Fishing around the island, i.e. Tarpon Bay, is spectacular, and tends to attract anglers by the droves.

Although we had spoken previously at length, I had Demetrius message me so I could include his story in conversational form:

"This was a weird weekday, as a couple of us left Sanibel on a friend's 'yacht' as he called it. It was a big fishing boat to us (over fifty feet). There were three of us, but there were supposed to be five. I'd never been out on a boat that big before. I remember it looked like rain, but (it) never did. We were out for a short while and were going to do some fishing, I remember the other two guys were talking about diving, but I don't recall (that) they ever did."

In retrospect, they were lucky that they didn't.

"We were out for about maybe two hours or so and both of the other guys were talking about heading back as the weather looked really off, but everything (the sea) was calm. I looked to my right and saw what I first thought was a log or something, but the color was off. (It was) brownish-red or reddish-brown: like that. It moved suddenly, and I could see suckers. It reached out and started lightly touching the boat all around, but (it) was never aggressive or anything, more than slightly curious, it seemed."

I explained to Demetrius at this point that the behavior he witnessed was common among octopi. They have chemoreceptors in their suckers that enable them to taste things. The animal – undoubtedly attracted to the smells of blood and bait – was most likely "tasting" their boat's hull to see if it was a sleeping whale, i.e. edible.

"One of the other guys saw it and said nothing, and the other guy (who) was on top of the cabin area did the same. The tentacle thing never jumped out of the water or anything, like in a horror movie. (It was) just curious and then went under and we could see something but were unsure what we saw – maybe the mass of the animal. I'm glad we weren't what it was looking for, as the tentacle was, no joke, around 30 feet or a little bigger. Again, at no time was the animal aggressive and maybe it was young as it seemed, in retrospect, maybe shy."

Shy or perhaps cautious. Octopi have brains proportionately larger than many mammal species. They're highly intelligent.

"If what we saw was the mass of the beastie, it was around 80 or 90 feet, I would guess, and from what I could tell, there was more (of the) tentacle underneath (submerged) as well as others. It just swam away under the Gulf waters. We agreed to say nothing as we figured everyone would think we were drunk and saw a sea monster (we forgot to bring beer and only had tepid Coca-Cola and Pepsi-Cola). Until I told you, I haven't told anyone (about) that encounter. I don't know if the others ever told anyone, but I doubt it."

Max: "Intriguing. As I recall during our first discussion, you said that the length of tentacle that was visible on the surface ranged from two to three feet in thickness. Is that right? Was the skin smooth, rough, textured? And do you remember how far offshore u were and the approximate date that this happened? I believe you mentioned it was 2014, and also that you called it in to the Coast Guard or Harbormaster, and that they said they'd had a sighting like that just a day or two earlier. Is that accurate?"

At this point, I'd provided Demetrius with an illustration to see if the size of what they'd seen was accurate as compared to their boat.

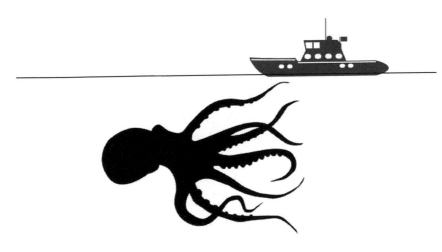

Approximate proportions of the *"Octopus giganteus"* observed off Sanibel Island, compared to a fifty-foot boat.

"Yeah, pretty much. It was around 2 feet maybe 3 feet across and smooth, I recall. We didn't tell the Harbormaster until around a week or so later, and he told us that the animal had been seen around there for around a month or so-- this was around mid-July as it was for two of our birthdays. Your drawing seems about right, Max. Yeah, the boat was around 50 or maybe 60 ft. – it was either 2013 or 2014 – I'm not sure anymore, as I was there both summers. We were a good 2 miles it seemed offshore. As I say mid-July, but don't remember if it was July 15 or 16 now. The one thing that has remained constant was that the animal was never aggressive in any manner – just curious like a puppy or kitten would be, which is why I thought maybe it was a baby."

Max: *"Fascinating. I would say it was probably more cautious. You guys were fishing. Were you putting out chum or using bait? I believe the smell is what attracted it and it wanted to see if the boat was edible."*

"Gee, the other guys baited the poles so I don't know what they were using to be honest. Thinking about it, whatever it was smelled awful and maybe that was (what) drew the monster in. I don't think he/she liked it as it left us and swam away..."

Max: *"So, no chum line though? Like in 'JAWS'? Or today, perhaps, more a frozen bucket of chum hung over the side, thawing and leaving a film of fish oil etc. on the surface?"*

Demetrius was unaware of any chumming being done, so most likely there wasn't. One thing he was certain of, however, was the identity of their curious visitor.

"I am certain it was an octopus. Once we were (back) on shore we went to the library, as one guy thought (it was) a squid. But no (images of) squid arms looked like what we saw – definitely an octopus."

Summary

Based on the witness's statements, I believe he saw what he says he saw. Moreover, he has two compatriots who can corroborate his story. The cephalopod in question must have been enormous, especially if they saw at least thirty feet of one arm, with more of it leading down to the shadowy mass of its body.

It makes sense that an animal like that would be lurking around Sanibel Island. There is an abundance of marine life, and one particular species that might well attract a predator like that would be Florida's resident population of manatees. Many of the sightings of huge octopi off Hawaii coincide with the spawning season for the region's green sea turtles (*Chelonia mydas*). Green sea turtles are among the world's largest chelonians, with big, breeding females able to top six hundred pounds. They are large, relatively slow, and not capable of putting up much of a fight.

To a hungry octopus, it's an ideal meal.

Now think of a manatee. They're like swimming pork rolls. They're slow, fat, blubber rich, and can top thirteen feet and thirteen-hundred pounds. And they're defenseless. As meals go, it doesn't get much easier than that.

Personally, I think Demetrius and his friends were lucky. Diving into the water at that time would have been suicide. But even without that, if the animal had mistaken their fishing yacht for a sleeping whale (an eighty-foot octopus would be capable of taking down an adult humpback) and attacked it, it would've soon discovered its mistake. But if, during its initial assault, it came in contact with a screaming, struggling *Homo sapiens*, it might have decided a few hors d'oeuvres were still worth the effort.

A scene like that would be beyond horrifying, and is eerily reminiscent of a chapter in *Kronos Rising: Kraken* (vol. 1), where I had a pair of monstrous octopuses lay siege to a big schooner named, appropriately enough, the *Rorqual*.

On a related topic, I find the Harbor Master's reaction disturbing. Once notified, he acknowledged that the creature had already been in the area for a *month*. The authorities knew about it. Does that mean nothing was done? Was anyone warned? Were steps taken to protect people? Did any swimmers, surfers, or paddle boarders disappear mysteriously during that time?

All questions that need answering.

Bottom line: I would be extremely cautious when plying the waters around Sanibel Island. The region's sharks alone are cause for concern. But if Demetrius's account is true, it is likely that this creature – and possibly others of its kind – come there regularly, or at least seasonally, to feast upon the area manatees.

And you do *not* want to be mistaken for one . . .

A giant octopus, emerging from its lair on the sea floor.

SANIBEL SEA BEAST

A year or so before Demetrius's encounter with what may well have been a real-life *Octopus giganteus,* David Carlin and his then-fiancé (now wife) Patricia had an encounter with a marine monster that may well have been the same behemoth, making its rounds. The incident took place right off Sanibel island, not far from the spot where the giant octopus appeared.

As I mentioned before, Sanibel is both an island and a city. Besides being a popular tourist destination, it is a wildlife sanctuary and home to a vast assortment of animal life, including the region's omnipresent resident manatees. It was the presence of these manatees that attracted the creature the unsuspecting couple encountered.

But unlike the previous incident, this time it was caught on film.

Or at least a portion of it was.

While fishing around Sanibel, Dave and Patricia pulled their boat into a shallow bay. They saw a pod of manatees approaching and, out of concern for the animals' safety, came to a complete stop.

Dave turned on his video camera and started filming the manatees. A moment later, something else appeared. Something huge. According to the commentary provided by the couple on their YouTube channel, this is what happened.

"Excuse the language we use in the clip. We were scared! It's either a massive Anaconda or a Sea Monster. Whatever came out of that water scared the life out of my fiancé and I. We were

fishing on our boat in the shallow bay area of Sanibel Island, FL, on October 6th, 2013 when we saw what looked like a bus speeding through the water. At first, we thought we were watching Manatee swimming which we see all the time but this animal was moving very fast and looked to be attacking something. All of a sudden, part of its body sprung out of the water and appeared to have something wrapped up. Then it was gone. We honestly don't know what it was but its head resembled a sea otter and the body looked like a giant 20 plus foot snake. If a cement utility poll was laying down horizontally, that would be the width and length of this sea creature."

I reached out to the now-married Carlins and did an interview with David to discuss their sighting in detail. He observed the creature approaching underwater – a dark shadow moving at a surprisingly fast speed. In fact, it passed right under the boat (note: water depth in that region is relatively shallow, averaging 16-24 feet).

As his YouTube video statement said, the predator was about the size of a bus, but only in length. It closed on the manatee pod, then something shot out of it, a part of its body that was, as described, the length and diameter of a utility pole.

The portion of its body wrapped around a young manatee, and the frantically struggling marine mammal was dragged under the surface, never to be seen again. Dave described the portion of the creature's body that broke the surface as being dark above, almost black, and white below. As indicated in his statement, he believes it was some sort of enormous snake of some kind.

Dave told me that there were some irregularities when it came to their video. He said that after they gave it to someone to download onto YouTube, the footage seemed to have lost quality. It was no longer in HD and a lot of details were lost. He sent me this still from his phone, which he said shows details the online video doesn't have. On the left side of the screen you can see a white form arcing over something, and under it is the face of the young manatee that was targeted. He believes that this is the pale underside of the creature's body, the moment before it struck.

Based on a frame-by-frame analysis of Dave's video, he is at least partially correct. The doleful-looking face is, indeed, that of either a manatee or some species of pinniped (seal or sea lion). Most likely, the former. I was able to determine, however, by viewing the video repeatedly in slow motion, that the whitish arch is not the underside of the body of the creature he and Patricia observed. Rather, it is a wall of water cast up by the force of its strike and arcing over the head of the manatee on the left. The manatee that was targeted was to the viewer's right of that one, or the middle one, if there were three clustered together.

Let's do a clinical, frame-by-frame review of what transpired that day.

In this frame, whatever it is that wraps around the hapless manatee appears as just a "bump" on the water. It is still covered by a thin layer of water at this point, and appears as a watery mound, more or less. I've indicated it by an arrow. Sadly, this book's black-and-white images do not do it justice, but there are enhanced color versions on my website. Also, I encourage you to see the Carlin's video online and take it full screen, then run through it frame by frame to get a better sense of what I'm demonstrating.

In this next frame, whatever this is has broken the surface and is wrapped around its target (presumably a manatee). Initially, many dismissed this video stating it was simply a manatee rolling on the surface, as they are known to do. However, if you look closely, you can see that whatever that is in the center has an almost rubbery texture to it, and an underside that is just visible. This suggests that it is comparatively thin in terms of its cross-section.

You can see it better in this closeup, despite a bit of graininess.

Now, *this* is where things start to get interesting. After Dave told me that something had happened to their video as it was being uploaded onto YouTube, I paid especially good attention to it. And I discovered that he was right. People can toss the words "conspiracy theory" around all they want, but the fact is that someone has deliberately blocked out a tiny portion of each of the next few critical frames of this footage.

When I say "blocked out", I mean that literally. There is an actual square of diffused pixels present on the screen. This is a form of censorship called *fogging*. It is done to obscure a portion of a frame or image to obscure it from the viewer. You've probably seen it on television when someone's identity needs to be kept secret. In this case, however, the fogging is master-fully done. It's so subtle that only someone really looking would notice it.

Unfortunately for whoever was trying to hide something, that someone happened to be me.

I don't know what they were trying to hide. I suspect it is details of the attack. Perhaps the startled manatee's face as it was seized. Perhaps details of the creature attacking it that would derail any attempts to dismiss the footage as "just a manatee rolling". But it was definitely done and on purpose. It's harder to show in black and white, but can you see it in the frame above?

How about now? Compare this to the previous frame and it should be noticeable. Keep this in mind as we move forward, because it's going to become more and more apparent.

Let's look at this frame Dave sent me. I've indicated the affected area with a square. That blackish portion forming a perfect corner with right angles is not an animal or an object. It's fogging, cleverly overlapped with the water splashing to cover up whatever was in that frame. I'm not sure how this as done – perhaps a second frame overlapping the first, but in my opinion, it's definitely been doctored.

In the frame above, the object that curled around the (presumed) manatee has begun to flatten a bit. That is indicative of it flexing/contracting and exerting downward pressure, i.e. pulling. And, again, if you look closely, that mysterious fogging box is still there (see closeup below). In fact, this is the "money shot". It's so obvious, even in black and white. It's about as close as one gets to a smoking gun. I don't know what someone wanted to hide, but it's in these critical few frames that would most likely confirm that not only is that hump not a manatee, but would give us the identity of its attacker.

In this next frame (above), whatever has wrapped around the manatee has started attempting to drag it under. The manatee is struggling, and the arrow on the left indicates its paddle-shaped tail breaking the surface as is flails. This indicates that the manatee on the left that had water arcing over it was not the one that was seized, but rather the one beside it. When the video is viewed, it becomes apparent that the central point, or hump, is pulling straight down, and the tail that breaks the surface is pulled down by it.

The fogging box is still there, but at this point has migrated over to the top of the dark hump (see the second arrow)

The two frames above are almost identical. The first shows that the fog-box (above the black hump) is now toward the left portion of the hump but is a bit diffused. The second shows the eyes of the manatee that was not seized (left arrow) and the hump of whatever seized the one next to it (right arrow).

This next frame (above) is also of interest. It appears that the attacking object was barely still visible, but there are now multiple areas of our "money shot" that have been fogged. Again, this was very well executed. I not only enlarged and enhanced the frame, I darkened it to make the areas of deliberate pixilation visible. See the arrows below.

Someone *did* not and *does* not want these frames visible. If Dave is right and his footage was altered in terms of definition, then, logically, whoever did that most likely also did this.

The previous two frames are relatively uneventful. The manatee has been dragged under amid a huge splash of water.

This frame and its closeup are important. A literal second after the strike and the manatee's tail is pulled under, an object appears on the right side of the object that seized the manatee, a few yards away (see arrows above). As the next few frames (below) show, it peeks above the surface for a split-second, and then is also pulled under.

Based on the first of these three frames, I believe the object popping up briefly is the head of the manatee or pinniped. It is struggling to get to the surface to breathe, and is then pulled violently back under. You can see dark circles at the bottom that appear to be its eyes, seen dorsally (from above) and the shape is consistent with the muzzle of a marine mammal like that.

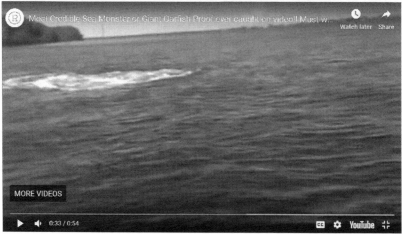

After that, the manatee is gone. The couple is rightfully scared and move away from the scene. But the question remains: what was it? What did they see and partially film, and why does it appear that someone felt the need to obscure the truth of what they filmed from the public?

Candidates

When considering this, we have to take into account the possibility of both known and unknown creatures. David believes what he saw was some sort of enormous serpent, something along the lines of a *Titanoboa*. He bases this on it wrapping around its victim and the whitish underbelly that he believes he saw. However, a lot can happen with all the adrenaline one experiences during such an occurrence, and as we now know, what he interpreted as the predator's underbelly in the frame is actually the water it displaced.

He was adamant however, that the thing he saw was whitish below and dark above. That is apparent from the footage.

Both he and his fiancé were also sure that the creature was as big as a bus, fast moving, and that something appeared to extend from it, which broke the surface as it wrapped around its target. That portion was described as being twenty feet long and as thick as a utility pole (for the record, said poles are over a foot in diameter).

A few additional points, however. Going by the points in the footage where the manatee's tail breaks the surface on the left, and its head bobs up on the right, we can see that the diameter of the object that wraps around it is approximately one-fourth the manatee's overall length.

Adult manatees in Florida range from 9-13 feet in length. David did say he felt this was a young manatee, so it could've been smaller. However, he also believed that the animal on the left was the one that was seized, when it appears that there was one to its right (our right) that was, in fact.

This makes it difficult, as we have no definitive size to work with. So, for the sake of being conservative, we will assume that the manatee (which may or may not have been an adult) was somewhere around 8-10 feet in length.

This makes the object wrapping around it at least two feet thick, possibly closer to three. But what was it?

After having interviewed Demetrius and heard about a gigantic octopus that explored the boat he and his friends were on, my first thought is that it was the same animal. Or, perhaps, another one.

It makes sense. Manatees are big, slow and defenseless, the "pork rolls of the sea" as I like to refer to them. There have been many reports of monster octopi appearing in Hawaii when green turtles come to lay their eggs. It makes sense that an opportunistic octopus (or octopi) would frequent the manatee-rich waters around Sanibel Island, taking advantage of the banquet that awaited them.

Octopuses are stealthy, cunning, and fast. One could easily blend in with the bottom, at least partly concealing its bus-sized length (around forty feet), jet toward its target, and then lash out with a tentacle two-feet-thick and snag its meal.

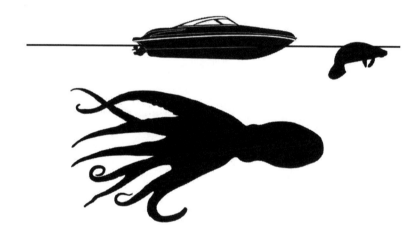

The manatee wouldn't have a chance, and would be hauled under, writhing and crying out, as it was hauled toward the cephalopod's waiting beak. Its death would be slow and agonizing.

Another possibility that looms large to me is that the Sanibel serpent was not an octopus, but rather, a large squid.

David told me that the thing he saw was four feet thick as it passed under his boat. An octopus forty feet in length would, in my opinion, be a bit wider than that, but perhaps if its tentacles were tucked tightly in a bundle as it jetted forward, it's possible.

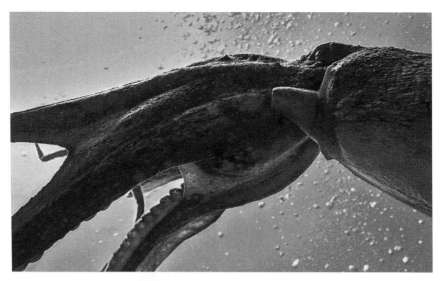

A giant Pacific octopus swimming backwards. Could something like this have been what passed under the Carlins' boat?

A very large squid would also be a possibility. A squid with a body four feet thick would be a huge and dangerous predator. Moreover, many predatory squid species like *Architeuthis* have a pair of feeding tentacles or "clubs", in addition to their eight arms. In the case of the giant squid the clubs have large suckers, each with a curved, cat-like talon in the center that digs into flesh and ensures a firm hold. They are kept retracted until prey is sighted, at which point they stick together like Velcro and shoot out like a spear toward the target. The palm-shaped ends of the tentacles open like a mouth, slamming into and ensnaring the victim, before dragging it toward the squid's hungry mouth.

It is possible that the portion of the attacker's body the Carlins saw shooting out was, in fact, a squid's attack clubs. The thickness and length make sense, and the rubbery portion that sort of flattens out as it seizes the manatee and drags it to its doom could also be that. Additionally, the underside of a squid's tentacles – and the arms of an octopus, for that matter – are typically a whitish color. This might well explain the serpentine appearance that David described.

With a squid as another distinct possibility, I put together a diagram mapping out how such an attack might have taken place.

Either of these represents intriguing and disturbing possibilities. Of course, there's always the possibility that David may be right. There may be some sort of immense serpent out there, or something else altogether. However, with another sighting having taken place around the same time and region that was – per the witnesses – a definite octopus, and with cephalopods known for seeking out easy to catch prey that provides a great deal of sustenance, I am inclined to think an octopus or squid is the most likely candidate for what the Carlins experienced.

Suffice to say, they were smart to avoid the water around there after that.

A Florida manatee showing a cluster of rake marks on its flank. Is it possible these scars have been caused by the clawed suckers of a squid?

THE THING IN THE CEMETERY

I saved this entry for last. I had to think long and hard about whether or not to include it in the book. I'd previously recounted it to *Into the Fray* host Shannon LeGro, who was (of course) enthusiastic about the idea, but I was leery about going public. There were several reasons for this. Chief among them was fear in its assorted incarnations. Fear of ridicule, of course, ranked high on the list. And that's justified. People reading this will invariably call me a liar or say that I was drunk or high, or that I imagined the entire experience. But far stronger than the fear of being perceived as a laughing stock is the lingering terror of what I experienced that night, coupled with the admittedly insane notion that someway, somehow, by me telling the tale there will be repercussions of some kind. Retaliation, if you will.

As you read on, I'm sure you'll laugh at that last part. After all, it's not like the undead have smart phones and Wi-Fi. Well, maybe the more civilized ones.

Oh, and just so we're clear; I don't drink and I've never done drugs.

That said, this is my story. You can scoff at it, make fun of it, or dismiss it out of hand. And that's fine. But you weren't there and you didn't see what I saw. If you had, you'd know it was no laughing matter.

The night in question took place in the summer of 1984. I lived with my family back then in the suburbs of what was, at that time, known as "Sensible Southwest Philadelphia". I was nineteen: tall and lean, and had been lifting weights and studying Ryukyu Kenpo karate for a little over a year. I mention this to make it clear that I was not some helpless child. I wasn't afraid of the dark and I could take care of myself. At least I thought I could. In fact, like most testosterone-riddled adolescents, I believed I was indestructible.

I had developed a habit of taking our family dog, a Doberman pinscher named Caesar, on long hikes into the woods of nearby Fairmount park. I did this once or twice a month, usually when the moon was full or close to it. It made it easy to see. It was thrilling; the forest was warm and alive, and I never saw another human being during our late-night walks. At least, not inside the park, proper.

My usual routine with Caesar was to leave the house and make our way down to the road bordering Cobb's creek. We'd follow that for a good half mile or more, then climb up and cross over an overpass that, on the opposite side, led into the woods of Fairmount park. We'd follow the forest trail for a stretch, maybe a mile or so on a guess, until we came to a very steep hill.

That hill bordered Mount Moriah Cemetery. Mount Moriah is an old cemetery. It was established in 1855 and is sizable – anywhere from 200 to 380 acres, depending on the source. Nowadays, the cemetery is in serious disarray. It has had no guardianship since the last member of the Mount Moriah Cemetery association died in 2004. It finally closed in 2011, and is now overrun with weeds and garbage, the latter dumped by disrespectful human beings. Tombstones have been shattered and knocked down and monuments felled. It's a sad thing; and those attempting to clean the place up find themselves facing an uphill battle.

Like most cemeteries, Mount Moriah has a reputation for being "haunted". In truth, it is a dangerous place. Drug deals and prostitution are common, especially nowadays. In May of 2020, the cemetery made headlines after the bodies of two murdered men were discovered there – deposited in a crypt.*

Mount Moriah's dilapidated "Button" gatehouse by Stephen Decatur
Button. Public domain image.

I don't know what the exact date was the night I had my
"experience". As I mentioned, it was probably on or around a
full moon during the summer of 1984. That most likely narrows
it down to around June 13th, July 12th, or August 11th. If I had
to take a guess, it was probably July or August, as I'd done the
same walk a few times before. Plus, it was warm out and the
leaves had not started to fall. I do remember that, due to stories
of packs of feral dogs attacking people in the park, I was carry-
ing a nightstick. I figured the Doberman could hold his own, But
I wanted something I could use to fend off aggressive canines,
in the event that we got jumped.

As luck would have it, we made it through the woods unmo-
lested. When we got to the hill bordering the cemetery (there
were no wrought iron fences on that side – I guess the design-
ers figured only a madman would attempt to scale a slippery,
leaf-strewn slope that was near vertical in places) Caesar and
I worked our way toward the top. The dog was beyond agile
and, after I let go of his leash, he made it to the top like a mountain goat. Between grabbing hold of his leash and holding onto

exposed tree roots at the edge of the drop-off, I managed to follow suit and hoisted myself up inside the cemetery.

We'd left the house around midnight (rather fittingly) so
it was probably thirty minutes past at that point. We followed
our usual path, which was to circle that portion of the cemetery via the graveled road until we got over to the Yeadon
side. At that point, the steep hill to our left that plummeted
down into the woods had completely leveled out. We could
cross through the woods on relatively flat ground. Then, once
we'd reached the town known as Yeadon, we'd hang a left
and take its streets all the way back home to our bordering
neighborhood.

As I recall, it was dead quiet that night. Pun intended.

Courtesy of the moonlight, the cemetery stood out in stark,
albeit black and white details. We were walking soundlessly
along, stopping periodically so Caesar could sniff something or
lift his leg, when I heard it.

It was a strange sound. I'd never heard it before nor since,
but it's one that is forever burned into my brain. It sounded liked
something was digging. Or, to be more specific, like something
was clawing at the earth. There were short breaks in between
each sound; I'd say three to four seconds.

I stopped in my tracks. In an instant, all the hairs on the back
of my neck stood up and gooseflesh popped up all over my body.
Of course, knowing I was walking through a cemetery at midnight was bound to stir one's imagination, and I immediately
scoffed and castigated myself.

*Dude, you've been watching too many episodes of 'Creature
Double Feature'. Seriously. Stop being a pussy and man up!*

I started forward again, moving slowly along the road, but
the noise continued. After a moment, I was able to pinpoint its
location. It was coming from an isolated tombstone, located
near the road to my right. The stone was big, dark, and obviously old, and I would know it again if I saw it.

The digging sounds were emanating from it.

At this point, I swallowed nervously and glanced down at my Doberman. Caesar seemed confused. He was looking around for the source, but didn't seem outwardly nervous. At least, not yet. The sound continued. It started getting a bit louder and I could feel the gravel beneath my feet vibrate a tiny bit with each impact.

I was about ten feet from the tombstone when it happened.

Suddenly, something burst up from the ground about three feet in front of the stone. It scattered the smattering of leaves that were there, and sprayed chunks of soil in every direction as it erupted up out of the earth.

It was a *hand.*

My heart leapt into my throat and the words, "Holy God!" slipped unbidden from my mouth. Then common sense kicked in and my brain went into instant denial. My peeled-wide eyes began to blink furiously as I tried repeatedly to clear my obviously messed up vision.

That's not a hand, I told myself. *It's just a ground hog or a big mole, maybe an insane squirrel, or a rabbit that somehow missed his turn at Albuquerque. You're imagining it! That's it, right?*

But as I stood there gawking, desperate to believe that what I was seeing was anything other than what I knew it was, the hand began to move. When it had first burst through the earth the fingers had been extended rigidly outward. Then, as I watched, it relaxed. The fingers and wrist sagged downward, like it was tired maybe. It was then that I got a good look at it.

It was big.

Probably half again as long as my own hand, with fingers twice as thick. The skin was a pale gray in color, at least in the moonlight, and was rather loose-fitting, like it was saggy or rotting off the flesh underneath. The fingernails were thick and rather long, but jagged-looking (I assume this was from digging through hard-packed dirt).

At this point, my adrenalized brain was moving at light speed. From the size of the thing's hand, I figured that whatever was attached to it was at least seven feet tall. Moreover, knowing that they put coffins in concrete vaults to protect them from being crushed by the weight of the soil covering them, anything powerful enough to not only survive that, but to actually be able to *dig* through it had to be immensely powerful.

My nightstick would have done nothing to it, and it would've snapped Caesar's neck like a twig. I knew two things at that point. The first was that I was looking at a vampire – a real one – emerging from its hiding place to feed. And the second was that we were about to die.

Having presumably recovered from its exertions, the hand started moving again. The fingers spread and it started tensing, twisting from side to side. I knew then that the rest of it would soon follow, and that once it saw me there would be no escape. A powerful fight-or-flight impulse came over me and I realized that fleeing was the only option. I had to make a break for it, but taking the long way through the woods leading to

Yeadon seemed like suicide. It would see me for sure and run me down.

Then, despite the terror coursing through me, the oddest thing happened. A scene from the Clint Eastwood movie, *Every Which Way But Loose*, popped into my head. It was the one where one of Philo's police adversaries is sneaking up on him in the woods and comes face to face with an angry rattlesnake.

I swallowed hard, nodded, and uttered the exact same line from the movie, "Feet don't fail me now!" Then I dove down the hill to my left.

It was a miracle I wasn't killed. The slope was literally a forty-five-degree angle and was lined with trees, boulders, logs, and leaf litter. But I was so terrified that everything I saw was moving in slow motion. I managed to dodge, duck under, leap over, and skirt tree trunks, branches, and huge rocks – any of which could have ended my life in an instant.

It was so surreal. I felt like I was in a scene from a movie as they came at me, so slowly that I was able to avoid them. My Doberman, who had stood there paralyzed when the thing erupted out of the ground, couldn't keep up with me. My adrenaline rush, coupled with the gravity-based advantage of running downhill, had me moving with inhuman speed. I could hear poor Caesar choking as I dragged him along.

We hit the forest floor at the base of the hill and kept running. I covered what must have been a mile, and only stopped because I was exhausted. I collapsed in the mud and ferns and lay there, gasping like a dying fish. Thirty seconds later, I sprang to my feet and looked back with fear-filled eyes. I was positive I'd see the thing coming after me, but it wasn't there; my suicidal sprint had apparently enabled me to escape its killing field before it set eyes on me.

Not one to stand on ceremony, I took off like a shot. I ran the rest of the way home in what was, for me, world record time.

When I burst into the house, I was acting like a lunatic. I kept babbling about what I'd seen while rummaging around for garlic powder, (which I literally dumped all over myself) bibles, crucifixes . . . anything I could get my hands on.

Two of my brothers started mocking me as I recounted my tale. The bolder of them said to me, "Yeah, right. That's bullshit. You either made that up or you saw an animal of some kind." When I told him, quite vehemently, that I knew what I'd seen, he added, "Okay, c'mon. We've all been through that area. We know the way. You're coming with us and you're going to take us to the spot and we're going to prove that you're an idiot."

I laughed maniacally at him and replied, "Screw that! I am *not* going back there! If you two wanna go there, be my guest. I'll describe the exact spot, even the tombstone. And when you *don't* come back, which you won't, I'll tell mom what happened to you."

At this point, they exchanged nervous glances and decided that maybe going there wasn't such a good idea after all.

I've never been back to that cemetery since. Not during the day, and certainly not at night. The people that I've told my story to in confidence think that I either imagined it or misinterpreted what I saw. The few who are into cryptids and such things have asked me, "How do you know it was a vampire?" My answer is simply that was the impression I got. One person said he didn't think so. He said it was something else; a ghoul or zombie, perhaps.

Another individual said it sounded like a creature known as a *Strigoi*. According to my research, said creatures are spirits that rise from their graves and gain sustenance by draining the blood from the living. They are essentially linked with vampirism. The word *Strigoi* is Romanian in origin and literally translates to, "One risen from the grave."*

I don't know about ghouls, zombies, and all that stuff. But I can say with full confidence that, if what I saw *was* a vampire, they look *nothing* like the romanticized versions we see

---

* https://en.wikipedia.org/wiki/Strigoi

in popular books and movies. This thing was no beauteous "Lestat" or "Edward". And there would have been no communicating with it. It was huge and horrifying, and would have made a meal out of Caesar and me if I'd given it the chance. I've experienced some scary things in my life. In my senior year of college, I came face to face with the body of a freshman who'd hung himself two days earlier. Between his greenish face, agonized expression, and the dried blood that had run from his rolled-up eyes, ears, nose, and mouth, he looked like something from a horror movie. I've also done the bungee jump (admittedly with style), and even had bullets whizzing past my head in a NYC nightclub, while somehow still having the presence of mind to grab a friend of mine and toss her out of the line of fire.

All those experiences were scary as hell, and on the first and third I experienced the same slow-motion effect I did in the cemetery (albeit to a lesser degree). But none of them were one tenth as frightening as what I saw that night.

Of course, I'll be the first to admit that there's a remote possibility that I imagined the whole thing. I can't imagine how, but maybe I did. Maybe I lost my mind for those few minutes. Maybe I saw something and my adolescent brain made it out to be something that it wasn't. I'd like to believe so; but I don't. I remember staring at that gnarly hand in shock and disbelief and trying *desperately* to convince myself that it was anything other than what I thought it was.

It didn't work. The hand and its talons didn't metamorphosize into a fuzzy bunny rabbit or a chubby woodchuck. It was what it was, and I am firmly convinced of what I saw.

Of course, if I'm right, that creature could be hundreds of years old. It certainly looked ancient enough. If you think about it, it had the perfect habitat for itself, lurking in or around graves where it could remain undisturbed, and coming up periodically to claim a victim.

Hell, it was an ideal place to dispose of bodies, too. Especially if you can take them deep enough. Who knows? There could be a collection of skeletons down there.

A couple of times I've jokingly asked my wife if she'd be willing to take a day trip to Mount Moriah. She's declined. I also asked one of my brothers, but he didn't seem very enthusiastic, either. The only person I've asked who was eager for such an adventure was Shannon LeGro.

Shannon is fearless. Of course, she has no idea what might be waiting for us.

It's all fine to want to see something for yourself. But it's something else when you realize you're staring into the eyes of death incarnate. And then it's too late.

If I *did* ever go back there, it would be high noon and I'd be accompanied by an armed team – and I'm not talking stakes and holy water – equipped with ground penetrating radar. That way, we could find the stone and see if the soil had been disturbed at some point. If the thing was gone and had, say, changed locations (which would make sense) there would still be evidence that it had at least been there. And if it *was* still there, well . . . hence the armed personnel.

Of course, in a situation like that I am *not* diving down any more hills. Not at my age. Screw that. I'd want the car running and a driver behind the wheel. Because, believe you me, at the first sign of that thing I'd be out of there like Wile E. Coyote, complete with a big Acme rocket strapped to my rear end.

And if the rest of said team had a lick of sense, they'd be hard on my heels.

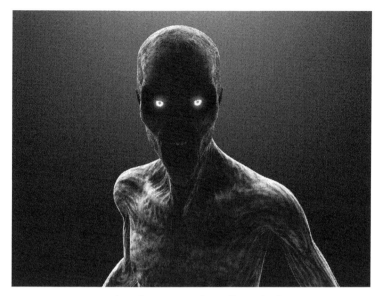

Artist's interpretation of a Strigoi.

THE END

We hope you've enjoyed Monsters & Marine Mysteries by Max Hawthorne. For updates on Max's next book and other exciting projects, go to www.maxhawthorne.com

Also, by Max Hawthorne

KRONOS RISING
KRONOS RISING: KRAKEN (Volume 1)
KRONOS RISING: KRAKEN (Volume 2)
KRONOS RISING: KRAKEN (Volume 3)
KRONOS RISING: DIABLO
KRONOS RISING: PLAGUE
Memoirs of a Gym Rat
I Want a Tyrannosaurus for Christmas

ABOUT THE AUTHOR

Known as the "Prince of Paleo-fiction", Max Hawthorne was born in Brooklyn and attended school in Philadelphia, where he graduated from the University of the Arts. He is the author of the award-winning KRONOS RISING novel series, as well as MEMOIRS OF A GYM RAT, an outrageous exposé of the health club industry. In addition to being a bestselling indie novelist, he is an amateur paleontologist, a Blog Talk Radio host, a Voting Member of the Author's Guild, an IGFA world-record-holding angler, and an avid sportsman and conservationist. His hobbies include archery, fishing, boating, boxing, and the collection of fossils and antiquities. He lives in the Greater Northeast with his wife, daughter, and a pair of enormous Siberian Forest Cats who, when they're not stalking Max's toes, sleep on his desk as he writes.

Made in the USA
Middletown, DE
31 August 2021